PILOT YOUR
OWN PLANE

PILOT YOUR
OWN PLANE

BY ROBERT SCHARFF

STERLING PUBLISHING CO., INC. NEW YORK

Acknowledgment

IN assembling this book, I had one overall purpose in mind—to present a book that would be both interesting and factual. To do this, I had a great deal of help. I would like to thank Edward Muhlfeld and Robert Parke for their permission to use material from *Flying Magazine* and *Flying Annual & Pilots' Guide;* Gil Gunnell of Gunnell Aviation, Inc. and Mike Connaughton of Mac-Aire Corporation for information on their flying clubs; Louis Mancuso of Mid-Island Air Service, Inc. for his help in teaching me to fly; the Goodyear Tire & Rubber Company for some data that appears in Chapter Two; and lastly, but most important, Leslie L. Thomason, Ed. D., who wrote Chapter 8 for this edition, and Bill Robinson and Jerry Kell of Cessna Aircraft Company for their overall help in making this book possible.

ROBERT SCHARFF
Stony Brook, New York

Contents

Foreword

By Skitch Henderson

NBC television star, composer, conductor, musician

Flying starts with doubt, the kind of doubt implied by the question: "Who, ME, Fly?" Who hasn't asked himself this question.

I assume you're among those people who have asked the question but for one reason or another have not taken that important first step toward getting involved in flying. Perhaps you've been intrigued by the idea that flying just might be for you, but can't quite picture yourself as a pilot.

Well, don't stop now. This book is for you. Author Bob Scharff has captured the real spirit of do-it-yourself flying —the challenge, the fun, the practicality, the surprising ease with which the average person may become a pilot, the incomparable thrill of a first solo flight—all are included here, along with down-to-earth discussions of basic flight principles, the technique and cost of learning to fly, and the personal and business uses for aircraft.

Every pilot has his own song to sing about flying. For me, there's exhilaration from just being in the air. It's fun to fly. I find that flying cleanses my mind and my soul.

There's a kind of music up there that gives a composer a challenge. When I can put that kind of sound on tape or on the air, I feel that I've done a good job of arranging. Many of my most successful arrangements have been developed—in the formative state—while I was behind the controls of a light plane on a cross-country trip. There is that essential time for meditation that is one of the best ways to produce really good music.

Flying is a blend of the sublime and the practical. It

9

broadens your personal horizons. It gives you new things to do—new places to go—new people to meet.

The sky is my greatest inspiration, my escape and my way of life. I only hope that others may share it. You may share it if you'll come fly with us.

Chapter 1

Who, Me, Fly?

You're all tied up in a bumper-to-bumper highway traffic jam and suddenly, through the window of your car, you notice a "little" airplane moving peacefully through the sky overhead. There comes a twinge of envy. He's not trapped as you are. And he's getting to where he wants to go at a good rate of speed. But that feeling of envy soon passes, since you quickly realize that the flying game isn't for you. No one is going to get you up into one of those flying matchboxes. The idea of defying the laws of gravity with one engine and a 36-foot wingspan borders on the insane. And anyone who willingly subjects himself to fickle Dame Nature high above the earth in one of those little airplanes has to be slightly frayed around his mental edges.

The pilot of that "little" plane high above you has some questions about your mental state of being, too. Why would anyone, like yourself, prefer to crawl along a highway, eating exhaust fumes, when you could be up in the cool, clean, uncrowded sky where he is? It's difficult for any pilot to understand why you seem to ignore a very obvious fact of our modern world—that the small, privately owned airplane, flown by average persons like yourself, is *not* just a passing fad. It has become an extremely practical and reliable means of pleasant, rapid transportation.

Of the nearly 100,000 civilian aircraft operating in the

11

United States today, only about 2,000 are commercial airliners, while the remaining are general aviation aircraft—mostly what you know as "little" airplanes owned by individuals or companies and flown for business or pleasure. These aircraft fly five times as many hours as are flown by all commercial airlines. The number of movements by general aviation aircraft in and out of airports controlled by Federal Aviation Agency towers far exceeds the movements of commercial airlines. And this includes only about 275 airports out of a total of more than 9,400 from which this type of aircraft operates.

Before going any further, it might be a good idea to state just what general aviation is and the types of flying it embraces. For all practical purposes, general aviation may be defined as all civil flying except that performed by the airlines; and it divides into the following four main areas of flying activity:

1. *Business flying,* consisting of corporate flying, is the use of corporation owned or leased aircraft for transportation of executives, company personnel and customers as well as light cargo manufactured by the company. Also covers specialized business uses such as pipeline inspection, site surveys for location of factories, real estate projects, mineral and petroleum prospecting, transmission line inspection, etc.

2. *Commercial flying* includes fixed base operations, air taxi, air charter and aerial applications as agricultural spraying or dusting, forestry patrol and the like.

3. *Instructional flying,* a vital part of general aviation, is accounting for an increasingly large share of the total as interest in learning to fly picks up.

4. *Personal* or *leisure flying,* which might be loosely defined as flying strictly for the fun of it, ranks second only to business flying in the general aviation total.

For a moment, let's return to that little plane you saw while you were caught in that traffic jam. Who is its pilot? Is he a steel-nerved superman in goggles and leather helmet? NO . . . he (or maybe the pilot is a woman) is just an average citizen, like yourself, perhaps wearing eyeglasses, with only average physical and mental ability. He may be a student, a farmer, a construction worker, an office employe, a professional man, or the president of a company. Or she may be a school teacher, secretary, or a housewife. Perhaps it's high time some of the myths about pilots were exploded.

Even today, when there are well over one million persons in the United States who have progressed at least to the point of soloing an airplane, the feeling persists among non-flyers that pilots are a breed apart—that they possess courage and abilities the common, garden variety of man can't hope to match—that they practice some mystic alchemy which overrules the laws of gravity. These widespread attitudes have combined to build around the pilot something we call *The Superman Syndrome.* The main symptom is a tendency to place pilots on a pedestal, there to be viewed as outstanding specimens of flowing-scarf boldness and mental and physical wizardry.

Pilots themselves must accept much of the blame for *The Superman Syndrome,* as they have too often thrown on a cloak of mystery and bravado. Even their most casual conversations about flying are confusing—and sometimes downright frightening—to the unknowing. Non-flyers who happen to get tuned in become more convinced than ever that pilots live in their own fourth dimension where mysterious forces lurk somewhere off the wingtips, just waiting for a chance to raise hell.

The main problem, however, lies in a lack of understanding among people who do not fly. Today—over 63 years after Kitty Hawk—more than 70 per cent of the adult population of the United States has never known the thrill of flying. Consequently, they don't relate flying to themselves or to people they know. They relate it instead to those who are bolder, or richer, or younger, or more capricious than they. In short, they relate flying to the

13

superman and nothing is further from the truth. Flying is for everyone—not supermen, or daredevils, or eccentrics, but everyone . . . people just like you and me.

WHY FLY?

But, why is private flying for me? The reason is really very simple: Flying is the *best* modern way to get where one is going—bar none. The airplane is a unique vehicle, and capable of launching its owner into a hundred totally different worlds in a week's time. And the worlds are not make-believe, they are real, in three dimensions.

Man has long been a creature of two dimensions, but what once was termed travel "across the length and breadth of this Nation" now is changing to "across the length, breadth, and *height* of this Nation." Personal travel habits have been geared to short distances. But, trips of hundreds and thousands of miles of distance, which once were prohibitive, are *now* short distances for the personal airplane. And, the airplane is becoming a natural method of transportation. The family uses it to see the Alma Mater play football on Saturday afternoon; Dad uses it to find that out-of-the-way fishing hole; or it provides transportation to Grandma's house on Thanksgiving Day. It may be used for no more than a Sunday afternoon drive around the "patch," getting no farther from the local airport than the established traffic pattern.

On family flying trips, very young children almost invariably succumb to the lulling drone of the engine and quickly fall asleep. Older ones can play such games as aerial "bingo" or may even take a turn at the control wheel. There's no reason why they can't do the latter; almost all private airplanes have dual controls. Teenage and grown-up passengers can take part in the aeronautical business of getting where you want by tuning in radio stations or helping with navigating; it's a good way for them to learn, and for the pilot to relax. When not involved in flying activities, the passengers may enjoy themselves by studying the slowly passing earth below, reading

14

a book, doing a little knitting, or just taking a nap. Family flying can be a magic carpet which offers something for every member—promotes exciting leisure together and expands weekends and holidays. To the flying family, it's not a matter of dreary miles to that favorite haunt, but a matter of a few, relaxing, pleasant and altogether different hours in the sky.

An airplane is a perfect, interesting way to entertain those very special friends of yours. For instance, the following true story shows how a foursome had a great time in the Mojave Desert, thanks to private flying:

There's plenty of fun to be found in San Francisco, but no matter how nice you have things you need a change occasionally. And my trouble, while living there, had always been that a weekend wasn't long enough to warrant all the bother and expense of getting somewhere really different. But all that was changed when my wife and I became friends with a couple who own an airplane. One Friday evening Bill and his wife were showing us slides of the Double J Ranch in Lucerne Valley, California, and I remarked that I sure would like to get away to a place like that. Bill said: "Let's all fly down there tomorrow." I made my usual objection to weekend trips, but Bill just laughed. "Come along on this one, and you'll never say that again."

At 8 A.M. Saturday, we met at the airport. While I loaded the baggage aboard, Bill filed a flight plan. By 8:15 we took off. I watched him closely, expecting to see a flurry of activity. But he just made a few checks, pushed in the throttle and took off. When we reached cruising altitude, he turned a couple of knobs, lit a cigarette, and leaned back to watch the scenery. "Is that all you have to do?" I asked. It looked easier than driving; certainly, a lot less tiring. And by 11:30 A.M. we were at Lucerne Valley in the Mojave Desert. Very impressive country, especially from the air. Bill radioed the Double J Ranch—it has its own landing strip—and a friendly voice gave landing instructions. I looked at the time and started figuring. Just

15

over three hours. It would have taken nine hours by car. And with the problem of connections, a weekend visit by airline would have been impractical. When I looked up, Bill grinned. He knew he had won a point.

We parked the airplane by the corral and, as soon as our wives saw the horses, they wanted to ride. And so we did—because one of the really nice things about the Double J was that it has no schedules, no rules. You can do what you want, when you want. A man from the ranch took our bags to our rooms, and a wrangler saddled up the horses. (Elsie, one of the wranglers, is a strong, wiry little woman who can outride any man I've met.)

After an hour of riding we were starved. But the Double J's delicious lunch quickly took care of that. Later, while we rested by the pool, I asked Bill how much it cost for us to fly to the ranch in his plane. I suspected it would be less than if we had traveled by airline, but I wasn't prepared for the shock of his answer. "The entire cost of the trip for the four of us, including our stay here at the ranch," he said, "will be considerably less than what airline tickets alone would have cost."

We enjoyed swimming until 4 P.M. when we decided to take another horseback ride. Elsie, the wrangler, told us how to get to a nearby movie set where Harley Mim's independent production company was filming a western, *Bullwhip,* and we rode out to it. It was so interesting watching a fight scene being filmed and later talking to the actors, we stayed at the set for over an hour. Then we rode back to the ranch.

A desert cookout was the next idea Bill suggested, and it was as good as the others. A man from the ranch packed up some steaks and trimmings and took us to a beautiful spot in the desert. I've rarely enjoyed anything so much. And I wonder what the coyotes thought when they heard us singing out there!

The next morning we went skiing at Big Bear Mountain. We hopped over there in the plane, and it took us less than ten minutes. We skied until lunch time, and then we went back to the ranch. After lunch, we lazed around the pool until time to check out. At 3 P.M. we took off for home and by 6 P.M. we were back at San Francisco—plenty of time for dinner. *A fitting footnote to this story:* The storyteller is now a pilot and is flying his own plane to other adventurous weekends. He is also the author of this book.

Not too many years ago, most families had only one automobile. In those days the "family" car was bought and used mostly for business by the breadwinner. By adroit and watchful scheduling the wife managed to gain possession for occasional errands. What really made it a "family" car was Saturday shopping, Sunday drives, and the annual family vacation. Today's "business/family" airplane is like this with some notable differences. Instead of being used as a method of commuting from home to office and back again, the business/family airplane can actually pay for itself in fast, dependable, straight-line business trips. It opens up new business territories and improves service in old ones. And it provides the kind of swift, convenient and comfortable business travel that protects the health and disposition of your traveler.

Have you ever gotten a little hot under the collar when finding it necessary to spend a few hours waiting around for an available airplane flight to your next destination? Or maybe you sometimes find the day just too short to meet all the demands of mobility in limited time allotted. Supposing your business demanded a day's routing something like this: First stop in the morning, a pair of bakeries in Grand Rapids, Michigan; later in the morning a bakery at Battle Creek, Michigan. Sounds feasible enough—but then for the afternoon let's throw in stops at Cleveland and Columbus, Ohio, and plan to bed down for the evening in Rochester, New York, ready for an early morning start the next day.

This is not a theoretical situation. It is the type of schedule which can be, and is, followed by the ever growing fleet of flying businessmen. This reporter actually traveled the schedule described above with one of the baking industry's airborne supplier-pilots. After spending a week of airborne movement with that successor to the Wrights, Curtiss, and Rickenbackers, it convinced this groundlubber that the private airplane can be a boon to the well traveled businessman. Commerical airlines built their position in the current transportation market with speed of travel. This same factor—along with the flexibility of travel schedules—is increasing the popularity of privately owned aircraft flying for business.

An extreme example of this time saving came to my attention the other day. A man whose office was in New York City had occasion to make five business meetings, two in Newark, New Jersey, one in Morristown, New Jersey, another in Bridgeport, Connecticut, and the last in a town on Eastern Long Island. All of these are within commuting distance of Manhattan but because of traffic congestion, at least two days and more likely three days would have been needed by ground transportation. Through the use of a private airplane all five meetings were made on the same day and this man was back at his home no later than he would have been from a routine day in the office.

Or consider the case of the insurance salesman in Nebraska who uses his own airplane to call on prospects in a four-state area. Even though he lives in a sparsely populated area, this salesman is among the top ten agents in his nationally known firm. Dollar values can be put on such travel savings but more important it multiplies the usefulness of individuals.

Multiply these examples by several thousand businessmen and you'll begin to get some idea of the scope of business flying today. If you're an engineer, geologist, rancher, salesman, printer, service technician, purchasing agent, accountant—you may well find that a business airplane is the answer to your service problem—or sales problem—or expansion problem. And don't forget the mental health side of the picture. Hundreds of busy busi-

18

nessmen are finding therapeutic relaxation in frequent short flights in the peaceful calm of the sky, physically separated from the hubbub of a modern day world. Talk about taking your mind off business—flying's the answer.

FOR WOMEN ONLY

What may be the most important development in aviation since Orville and Wilbur Wright got the first airplane off the ground is just taking off around the nation. Women are discovering the airplane—60 odd years after it was invented by men. Just a few years ago the ratio of women to men students at flight schools was almost zero to 100. Today about 7 per cent of the people who hold student pilot's licenses are women. More important than numbers of women is the type of woman who has turned to the airplane.

In sharp contrast to the small covey of woman fliers of the thirties and forties wrought in the image of Amelia Earhart, today's woman pilot is 99% pure American housewife and mother. Accused in the fifties of doing more to hold back private flying than the laws of gravity, the American wife in the nineteen-sixties—taking to the air in record numbers for the first time in history—is now doing more for the popular acceptance of flying than any man ever imagined.

If flying seems complicated to you now, just remember your first experience in driving a car. Flying, like driving, is a matter of getting used to a few simple principles, a few simple controls, and a few simple instruments. Ask any woman who's bothered to really check into it and you'll soon find out that fear of flying is mostly based on myth and misinformation. Like the 50-year-old mother of four who recently learned, you will probably be "amazed at how simple flying really is."

Think of it this way, you're not checking out in a supersonic, intercontinental bomber, you're simply flying a private airplane which represents modern-day transportation in its simplest form. Chances are you'll get your chance at the controls when you're flying with your husband. Don't miss it; it can open a whole new world to you. Flying, like many new national pastimes, has captured the imagination of great numbers of people, both young and old. There's no reason in the world why you wouldn't make a good pilot and share in the rewarding experiences which flying can bring to the entire family.

HOW SAFE IS PRIVATE FLYING?

There was a time when aviation was *not* considered safe. Anyone defying the laws of gravity in a plane was considered some sort of a nut. But, today, flying is surely one of the safest means of transportation. I am not going to give any statistics as to the safety merits of private flying vs. auto travel because there actually is no way to correctly compare the two. However, the real story of general aviation safety lies not in statistics but in the changes that have come about in recent years in airplanes and the people who fly them. These may be broken down into three general categories:

1. *Extensive design improvements* have made airplanes easier to fly.

2. *Improvements in aircraft equipment* have made the pilot's job simpler and safer.

3. *Better instruction methods and pilot aids* have vastly improved the capabilities of the man behind the wheel.

Today's private aircraft bears little relationship to its older brothers, which were designed primarily for the skilled pilot who was interested in sport flying and acrobatics and had little need for long-haul travel. However, the entire concept of the private airplane has changed. Today's airplane has a new mission, cross-country flying —transporting people or cargo from here to there as quickly, easily and as comfortable as possible. To fit this new mission, flying qualities of private planes have been radically changed. The emphasis has been on making the product more stable, safer, more comfortable, and simplified to the point where flying—contrary to public belief—requires little more physical skill than driving an automobile. As you read further in this book many of these design improvements will be discovered.

Safety is of the utmost concern not only to people who fly airplanes but also to those who make them. Manufacturers pay constant attention to improvements which enhance the air-worthiness or safety of their products. All manufacturers also work closely with the Federal Aviation Agency, which—among its many duties—establishes standards for producing and operating aircraft with the highest possible degree of safety. Progress will continue to be made as manufacturers strive to improve their product—to make it more safe, more practical, easier to service, simpler and easier to use. Manufacturers, the Federal Aviation Agency, and other interested parties will also continue their efforts to up-grade the capabilities of pilots and encourage the development of new aids—such as simplified pilot compartment designs—which will promote safer flying.

Most air accidents are man caused. Federal figures show that, of all aircraft accidents involving injuries, virtually all are caused either directly or indirectly by pilot error. Thus accidents are caused not by the complexity of an airplane, nor by the third dimension within which it operates, but rather (as with all accidents) by a human being who did something he knew better than to do.

The risks inherent in an airplane or any other moving vehicle will never be eliminated as long as people—with all their frailties—are operating them. But a well-built and well-maintained airplane in the hands of a competent and prudent pilot makes flying equally as safe as any form of transportation. But, for anyone really interested in statistics, you are—mathematically—quite a bit safer flying even the smallest airplane than you are driving your car to the airport.

Who, me, fly? This simple statement is intended to dramatize the obvious—that most everybody should investigate personal flying . . . because it's safe, simple and sensible. It offers a refreshing new look at the world below. You feel a new sense of freedom and gain a new perspective. You get a proud feeling of achievement as you sharpen your flying skill and knowledge. You gain new confidence . . . your future broadens . . . and the image of the whole flying family becomes more interesting, more exciting to friends, neighbors and business associates. You'll no longer be just one of the families in the neighborhood . . . *you'll be a flying family!*

You ask, "Who, me, fly?" Sure. You can start tomorrow!

Chapter 2

The Business of
Learning to Fly

THE trouble with the very first man who wanted to fly—
a fellow named Icarus who, you may recall, pasted some
feathers to his arms with wax and jumped out of a prison
tower—was that he didn't have enough information about
flying. Today, of course, the aviation industry is working
with ideas and materials that represent rather significant
improvements over feathers and wax. Yet, there are many
people who would like to fly, but hesitate simply because
they don't know how to go about taking the plunge and
getting started. Well, this chapter won't teach you how
to fly, but we hope that it will help to remove that first
hurdle by answering some of the questions most asked by
people who are "thinking of learning to fly."

WHERE DO I GO TO LEARN TO FLY?

The prospective pilot's first consideration will be to
find competent instruction. This may come in the form
of a friend who is an instructor pilot or it may be found at
a small aircraft service or flight school (referred to as a
"fixed-base operation"), on a local airport, or it may be
from one of several hundred well-equipped flight schools
whose comprehensive training program all but guarantees
a private pilot's license to those willing to put in the nec-

essary time and effort. The Yellow Pages of your telephone directory often list several such schools under "Aviation Instruction" or "Aircraft Dealer." Nearly all aircraft dealers offer flight instructions. Or you may visit your local airport or airports and inquire there. In addition, leading general aircraft manufacturers usually have a listing of their dealers who operate flight schools and will be very glad to send the names in your area.

Some flight courses will carry the notation "FAA Approved," which means that the school has met certain minimum requirements for physical facilities and flight and classroom equipment set by the Federal Aviation Agency. (All civil aviation is regulated by the FAA.) But the fact that a school may not rate as "FAA Approved" does not mean that the quality of instruction won't be as good or better than an approved one—that is up to the individual flight school operator. Ask some of your flying friends about the school at which they learned to fly. Their advice is usually very good.

Once you have the names of a couple of schools, call them and make an appointment to visit them. While there, ask questions about the school and its method of operation. Also try to meet the instructor that you will be assigned. A compatible relationship between you and your instructor will, of course, build your confidence and make your lessons much easier. While it is not necessary to always fly with the same instructor, it's usually easier to learn from one man's method of instruction.

HOW MUCH DOES IT COST TO BECOME A PILOT?

Actually, because of the many variables—the size of the airplane in which choose to learn, the type of course, local costs, the number of hours you need to develop the required proficiency—it's rather difficult to give an exact dollar figure. In a recent survey of the United States, basic figures reveal that the cost for about 90% of the recent private pilots ranged between $600 and $800. But for

24

more exact information in your area, call or go to a local flight school and ask them. Using their rates and computing them against the official requirement for a license, they will be able to tell you in advance approximately what the total cost will be.

You should know that there will be two different cost figures—one for "dual" instruction time and one for "solo" time. The solo fee will be the lowest and, actually, you will simply be renting the airplane in much the same way you rent a car—with all operating costs included in the per-hour rental fee. For "dual" time the price is higher, with the extra amount providing the certified flight instructor (CFI) who will go along. (Some flight schools offer a special so-called "solo course" which averages about $160.) It's important to realize that you pay only for the time you actually are at the controls of the airplane.

A point to remember in holding down the cost of learning is to fly as often—and as regularly—as possible. The pilot who takes lessons three times a week will learn faster than the one who goes for only one lesson a week. Reason: the coordinated skills are more easily grasped, and not as rapidly forgotten, with regular flying. I first found this out when, after a few widely spaced lessons, I went the whole route—from my first real airwork lessons to well beyond soloing in one concentrated 14-day spurt.

Recognized ground schools are also available in most communities where flight training can be obtained. Although there is no requirement that a student attend a ground school, it is generally recommended and worth the little extra cost. The ground school course usually covers pre-flight facts for the new student, an easy to understand discussion of aerodynamics; meteorology; the flight computer, a device used by pilots to compute airspeed, distances, wind effects, fuel consumption, and the like; navigation through the use of detailed maps and charts; radio navigation; and Federal Aviation Agency regulations pertaining to the private pilot. Upon completion of this course, students are equipped to take the written examination given by the FAA which assures that they are well-grounded in the basics of flying.

You may want to finance your training. For example, it is possible at certain schools to finance your lessons for as low as $10 per week for a complete private pilot's rating, including ground school. This could also be a factor in choosing a flight school that has such a program. You can check into this on your initial contact.

If you buy a new airplane, flight instruction is sometimes given free as part of the deal. You may not want to make this big an investment right off, but it's a point to be considered. You might also check on flying clubs in your area. Some clubs prefer licensed pilots but many are interested in flight training. Remember that while any licensed pilot can explain the fundamentals of flight to a beginner and even let him handle the controls, only flight time obtained with a CFI will count toward the private license.

Frankly, learning to pilot an airplane is not cheap. But, then, you probably have already guessed this. On the other hand, it isn't so expensive as you may think. For example, if you're only a moderately avid golfer, skier, or bowler, your expenses for just one season probably would come close to covering the cost of obtaining a private pilot's license. And when you amortize the value of learning to fly over a lifetime, you'll see what a bargain it is!

HOW LONG DOES IT TAKE TO LEARN TO FLY?

Government regulations covering pilot licenses are specific about minimum requirements but, at the same time, leave much to the judgment of the instructor. For example, the instructor has the say-so when a student can begin to fly solo. When he is satisfied the student can handle the plane safely and knows the appropriate flight rules and regulations, he endorses the student certificate for solo flight. An average student can expect to receive solo endorsement after 8 to 12 hours of dual instruction.

Once you're OK'd for solo, you can pretty much go any place at any time you want—provided the instructor feels you are competent for the particular trip. You can even fly your own business trips. The one restriction is that you may not carry passengers.

For the private license—the one that permits you to carry passengers and make your own decisions about whether you are proficient enough for a given trip—the FAA rules are specific. To be eligible (from the time standpoint) to take the private license exams you must have a total of at least 40 hours' flight time; of this at least 20 hours must be solo time and of these 20 at least 10 must be longer flights (up to 100 miles or more) from one city to another (they are called "cross-country" flights). As we said, these are minimums and the average student often requires a bit more.

How long does it take to accumulate 40 to 60 hours? That's largely up to you and the instructor. The consensus is that 2 to 3 hours' flying time per week is about the best learning rate—with more hours during weeks when cross-country flights are made. This would mean four to six months to get the private "ticket." But it is possible to do it in just a few weeks, while some people choose to fly for a year or more on their student licenses before taking the private license tests.

AM I TOO OLD . . . TOO YOUNG?

There are minimum age requirements—16 for a student license and 17 for a private "ticket"—but nothing in the regulations about a maximum. In fact, assuming continued general good health, advancing years have little to do with a person's ability to fly safely. Just to prove the point, the owner-operator of a small airport near Akron, Ohio, is in his 80's and flies his own plane every day. He learned to fly from aviation pioneer Glenn H. Curtiss way back in 1910.

DO I HAVE TO HAVE
A PHYSICAL EXAMINATION?

A medical exam, by a physician designated by the FAA (your flight school has the names of the nearby Aviation Medical Examiners), is required every two years. For a student (and later, private) pilot certificate you must have a "third-class" physical certificate. This requires the simplest aviation medical examination and compares roughly to a physical given for an insurance policy, although the vision requirements are higher. (If you wear glasses, you'll have no trouble as long as they correct your vision to 20/30 or better. Color blindness is a bit of a problem since some aspects of flying require color identification. The usual procedure in this case is not a medical rejection but simply a license restriction on certain kinds of flying.)

At present, you can be disqualified for problems with the nervous system, certain heart ailments or diabetes requiring insulin or other drugs. For lesser disorders, you may apply for the special issuance of a medical certificate. You will have to show that you can perform the duties under the airman certificate you hold, or for which you are applying, in a manner that will not endanger safety in the air. In other words, physical handicaps are not automatic barriers. As a matter of fact, there are countless pilots who are handicapped or crippled in some way. Only the ability to control an airplane counts.

If you are currently in the Armed Forces, you'll be interested to note that the FAA has designated senior flight surgeons on specified military posts, stations and facilities as aviation medical examiners. Check with the medical department of your facility concerning this.

ARE THERE OTHER QUALIFICATIONS?

There are very few qualification requirements for a private "ticket." One regulation, however, says only that an applicant for it must "be able to read, speak and understand the English language . . ."

From a practical standpoint, there is some math involved in flight planning and navigation, but nothing very complicated, and a portion of your training will be given to making sure you can work these problems. You need not be a mechanic or possess any special mechanical skills or aptitude. Nor do you need the physical coordination of an athlete. Just about anyone who can learn to drive a car can learn to fly. Actually—corny as it may sound—the three basic requisites to becoming a pilot (and a good one) are common sense, a desire to learn how to fly, and a willingness to stay within the boundaries of both flight regulations and your own piloting ability.

IS IT HARD TO LEARN TO FLY?

Yes . . . and no! Because there is quite a bit to learn, it will take some time and some concentration. It will certainly require more of you than learning to drive a car, for example. But what you will need to learn is not especially difficult—not nearly so difficult or complicated as most non-fliers think—and it can be mastered by practically anyone who is willing to devote just a little effort to it. Actually, many instructors claim that the major problem most beginning pilots have is the unlearning of old or bad habits of auto driving.

An important factor in learning to fly is that you'll be doing all your learning under the supervision of a highly qualified, licensed instructor. And because flying is taught on an individual basis, the instructor can and will customize the course of instruction to suit you.

There are two aspects of learning to fly—the actual "driving" of the airplane, and the "book learning." You will learn to "drive" by "driving"—actually handling the controls of the airplane yourself. Under the supervision of your instructor, you'll not only learn how to take off, land, and fly straight and level, you will learn how to make the plane do just what you want it to do and how to handle any emergency—including the very remote possibility of engine trouble in flight and forced landings.

The "book learning" covers flight planning, navigation, radio procedures, flight rules and regulations and the weather. By the time you're ready for your private license, you will be a competent pilot. The experience of future flying hours will certainly teach you more, but you'll be well equipped with the basic knowledge and skills necessary for safe flying.

HOW DIFFICULT ARE THE TESTS?

There is no test for a student certificate. But before a private license is issued, the student pilot is required to pass two tests.

The first is the written theory exam which is a long one—takes up to four hours to complete. You have to know your stuff to pass it. However, the instructor will do everything he can to make sure you do know, and if you have learned reasonably well you shouldn't have any trouble. It is largely a practical exam in which you will be asked to work out the details—navigation, weather, estimated times, fuel requirements and the like—for a mythical flight. You will have done it all before in planning the cross-country flights you actually will make—and there are no trick questions.

You may take the written test any number of times (in other words, you aren't "washed out" for failing), but it's always best to study harder beforehand and make it the first time. The minimum passing grade is 70 per cent.

After receiving notification (a grade slip from the FAA) that you've passed the written test, you're ready for the second exam—the flight test which is a practical demonstration of your flying ability. In this flight check-out examination, you take an FAA inspector or designated pilot examiner (a flight instructor designated by the FAA to give flight tests and issue certificates) for a "ride" to show him that you can handle the plane safely. Actually, the check ride is in two general phases: aeronautical skills and cross-country knowledge and techniques. Necessary skills must be exhibited in pre-flighting, starting, taxi techniques, run-up, straight and level flight, turns, climbs, glides, normal and cross-wind take-offs and landings, stall recovery, and simulated forced landings, and one short or soft-field take-off and landing. Frankly, the flight test is a difficult exam because no one wants an unsafe pilot endangering the lives of passengers. But it's not hard to pass the test. The reason is that your instructor won't "sign you over" for the check flight until you are ready for it. As a matter of fact, many instructors put their students through a simulated check flight just to make sure the test can be passed.

After successful completion of the check flight, the inspector or examiner will write out a temporary certificate and you can start exercising the privileges of a private pilot until your license is received in the mail. But, to answer the question—yes, the tests for your private license are difficult. They have to keep flying safe. But don't let the word "difficult" throw you. Learning to keep your balance on a bicycle once seemed pretty difficult, too.

WHAT ARE THE VARIOUS TYPES OF FLYING LICENSES I MAY OBTAIN?

Pilot licenses are "graded" just like automobile drivers' licenses. While some of the following information may be repetitious, let's look at the various licenses you may obtain:

Student Pilot. No test required. A student license is like a driver's permit and it allows the student to obtain the required amount of solo flight time prior to his flight test for a permanent license. It is valid only when endorsed by a CFI as "OK for solo" and accompanied by a medical certificate. A student pilot may not carry passengers.

Private Pilot. This is the first, and most common, of the pilot ratings and is the equivalent of an automobile driver's license. A private pilot may carry passengers and fly for pleasure or business. He may not fly for hire, although passengers may share expenses.

Commercial Pilot. Requirements are more stringent than for the private license, as this rating is equivalent to a chauffeur's license. A commercial pilot may fly and carry passengers for hire—in other words, fly for a living.

Air Transport Rating (ATR). It carries the same privileges as a commercial license but involves greater flying proficiency and a stiff physical. It is the highest pilot rating and is required mainly for airline and corporate flying.

DO I NEED A RADIO LICENSE?

An FCC permit is required to operate any transmitter since you are, in effect, an individual radio station. The permit costs two dollars, but no exam is required. Just send to the Federal Communications Commission, Gettysburg, Pennsylvania 17325, for a Restricted Radio Telephone Operator Permit application form. If you do not use a transmitter (as when flying to and from airports without control towers), there is no requirement for a permit—but then you may not be getting the most benefit from using the airplane as a means of cross-country transportation, either.

WHAT IS THE NEXT STEP?

Yours. This has been only an introduction to the steps necessary to join us who have already taken them and are now having the fun of traveling as the crow flies and looking at the world as the eagle sees it. Come on up; the air's fine.

A

Typical of aircraft used for training is this two-place Cessna Model 150.

Airplane on floats or skis becomes a real workhorse in many areas of the country.

B

Panel above contains basic flight instruments, plus C
radio and navigation receiver.

Wing flaps and "tricycle" landing gear, illustrated
below, are among many design improvements that
have simplified flying. D

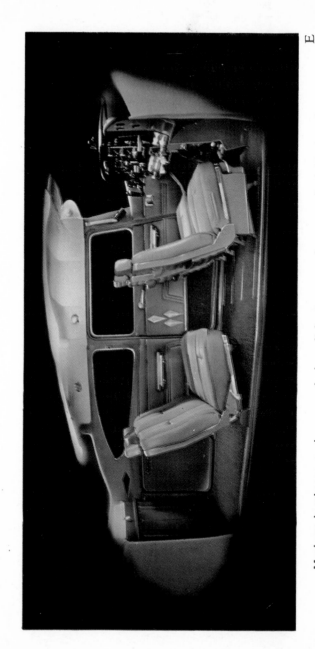

Modern business and personal aircraft feature spacious, comfortable interiors.

E

Thrill of a first solo is topped off with presentation
of a handsome trophy.

F

Interior of two-place trainer airplane.

G

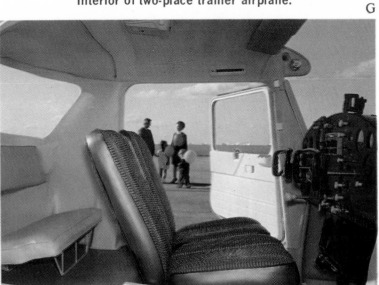

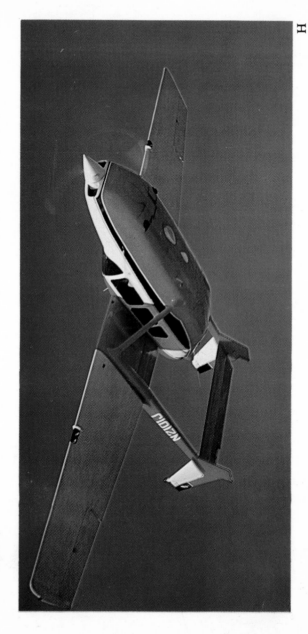

Twin-engine aircraft, such as unique Cessna Super Skymaster, are gaining in popularity for both business and pleasure uses.

Personal airplane opens the door to family travel.   I

Businessmen gain mobility and avoid being tied to transportation schedules through use of company airplane.   J

Chapter 3

What Makes an
Airplane Fly?

WHAT keeps an airplane up anyway? Why doesn't it fall out of the sky? As odd as these questions may sound here in the Twentieth Century, it must be remembered that the *application* of the physical laws that govern the principle of flight of heavier-than-air vehicles (airplanes) was put into practice a relatively short time ago. Many people simply have not been exposed to the simple explanation of the principle and its application. As a result, lots of people just accept the fact that airplanes *do* fly without understanding *why*. But, let's remedy all that right now since it's important for the would-be pilot to know what makes an airplane fly.

The place to start the explanation is with the air around us. It has weight—or pressure—which pushes against everything within the earth's atmosphere. When an object, be it animal, vegetable or mineral, is standing still, the air pressure is distributed equally over its entire surface. But when an object moves, the air around it moves, too, creating an unequal distribution of air pressure. This disturbance or redistribution of air pressure causes things to happen. For instance, a child running by a desk can cause a paper on that desk to sail up into the air in the wake of his path. What happens here is that the disturbed air trailing him travels over the *top* of the paper faster than under the *bottom* of the paper. Since fast-moving air has less pressure than slow-moving air, the air beneath the paper is now pushing *up* harder than the air on top of the paper is pushing *down*. The effect of this is called *lift*. It's the way a heavier-than-air object like an airplane is able to defy the laws of gravity.

Perhaps the most graphic illustration of lift can be observed in the bulged contour of the fabric top in a convertible type of automobile at high speed. This is especially noticeable on older models that have a rather loose fitting canvas top. It is lift that causes the bulged contour.

In the case of an airplane, the wing provides the lift. The airplane wing is not flat like a piece of paper. The top of the wing is arched up in a curve. It is thick near the front, or leading edge, rising in a curve and then thinning down to a sharp edge at the rear, called the trailing edge. The bottom of the wing is nearly flat. As the wing moves through the air, the air below the wing is disturbed very little while the air above the wing has to go over the curved top. Since the shortest distance between the leading edge of the wing and the trailing edge is a straight line, the air above the wing has to go farther than the air below. So top air has to go faster to meet the stream of air at the bottom. As the air speed increases as it goes over the wing, the pressure on the top surface decreases. On the other hand, the pressure on the bottom of the wing remains the same or increases slightly and pushes the wing upward, or provides lift to overcome the plane's *gravity*. (Gravity is the total weight of the loaded airplane and is the force which tries to push the airplane back down to the ground.)

Of course, in order to have any lift at all, the plane must be in motion. This is caused by the propeller, which bores into the air like a screw forced into wood or like a boat's propeller blade into water. This force, which is called *thrust*, gives the airplane its forward motion and keeps the air moving over the wings creating lift. The airplane's power plant (engine) supplies the energy to turn the propeller.

34

Another factor affecting the flight of an airplane is *drag,* which is really the resistance of the air as it strikes and then passes over and around the craft. In other words, the airplane must push the air out of the way to pass through it.

When an airplane is in steady flight, the four forces acting on it must more or less balance each other—lift equals gravity and thrust equals drag. On the take-off the lift must be greater than the force of gravity. In order to increase speed while in the air, the thrust must be greater than the drag.

THE ANATOMY OF AN AIRPLANE

Aside from the fact that Twentieth Century America grew up in the age of the automobile and has grown intimately accustomed to them from babyhood on, the basic operation of an airplane is *fundamentally* as simple as driving a car. It might seem strange at first, but flying, in a great many respects, *is* like driving a car. What makes it different and more fun is the fact that it takes in an additional dimension.

Before beginning any actual flight instruction, you should familiarize yourself with an airplane and its controls. While there are several different types and makes of airplanes, they are all made up of only five major parts: wing, power plant, empennage (tail section), landing gear and fuselage. (An automobile has corresponding components to power plant, fuselage and landing gear.)

THE FUSELAGE. The major components of the airplane are mounted, in their respective positions, on the fuselage or body. In addition to providing a rigid structure on which to mount the aircraft components, it also contains a comfortable compartment for the pilot and passengers. In the pilots' compartment are located all of the flight controls (usually in duplicate), "steering wheels," instruments, brakes, radios, and equipment needed to maintain complete control of the aircraft at all times. In modern airplanes, carefully designed interiors

35

surround the pilot and his passengers with all the comfort and utility features found in a new auto—body-contoured and adjustable seats of the vertical reclining bucket design, seat belts, glove compartment, carpeting, color-harmonized fabrics and paneling, and many other items (including ash trays and cigarette lighter) which permit the pilot to fly in complete comfort. And there is a very efficient heater for winter flying, and air vents for hot summer days. However, the air temperature drops about three-and-a-half degrees per 1,000 feet, so flying is one sure way to beat summer heat.

Luggage space in most business/family planes is quite adequate; weight is the limiting factor. Usually you can carry around 150 pounds along with four persons; more, if your passengers are children. Leg room is also adequate for the tallest pilot. Visibility that provides pilot and passengers with a panoramic view is available. In some airplane models, side windows, a rear window and a large wraparound windshield literally encircle the cabin with a "wall of windows" giving full 360° view. An optional rear-view mirror is often added for the pilot's viewing convenience.

THE LANDING GEAR. The primary function of the landing gear is to support the aircraft during the take-off run, landing, taxiing, and when parked. The tricycle landing gear—now standard on all except a few special-purpose airplanes—has done more than any other design change to make flying easier and safer. It makes ground handling easy, provides positive steering with the nose wheel, improves directional control during take-off and landing, and permits "drive-on" landings.

On most modern airplanes, the left and right wheels of the main landing gear are equipped with individual hydraulic brakes which are operated by applying toe pressure to the rudder pedals. A separate handle is used to set the brakes for parking, just like the parking brake on your car.

THE WING. The wing is the largest surface on an

airplane. As we have discussed, it gives the airplane the "lift" it must have to leave the ground and to sustain flight. The five parts of the wing are: the leading edge, trailing edge, ailerons, wing flaps, and tip.

The ailerons are located on the trailing edges at the ends of each wing. They are simply movable, controllable portions of the wing. They move in opposite directions and are controlled by a control wheel (steering wheel) in the cabin. When the control wheel is turned to left or right (just like a steering wheel), the opposite aileron moves *down* and the corresponding aileron moves *up*. The downward deflected aileron creates a new shape (or camber) for the wing. This results in an area of lower pressure above the wing. This pulls the wing up. Naturally, the other wing, with an inverted camber, goes down. When this happens, the airplane banks (turns) in the direction the control wheel is turned, right or left. That is, if the control is turned to the left, while the airplane is flying level, the left aileron will tilt upward, reducing the lift, and the right aileron will move downward, increasing the lift. In consequence, the right wing will rise, and the plane will be tilted or banked to the left. The total lifting force of the wing will then no longer be exerted vertically upward, but will be pulling the airplane somewhat to the left, producing a left turn. Phrasing it in another way, the airplane is "lifted" around the turn.

As an important safety feature, most general aviation planes are equipped with large flaps which provide excellent control during landing approaches and permit landing at very slow speeds. These flaps are set along the trailing edges of the wings, between the ailerons and the fuselage. These serve to change the lifting capacity of the wing by changing the shape or area of the wing surface. A control is provided in the cabin to lower the flaps into various down positions. These positions are referred to as degrees of flap extension; such as 10°, 20°, 30°, 40°, etc. When the wing flaps are lowered, they provide more curved surface to the upper camber of the wings. This decreases the pressure on top of the wing and allows slightly more pressure to build up under the wing. Thus, lift is increased. However, as the wing flaps are extended into the airstream to increase lift, they also cause additional drag. This drag increases with the down position of the flaps; the greater the flap extension, the greater the drag.

Aircraft engineers make use of the lift-to-drag ratio of wing flaps for two different purposes during the flight operation of an airplane. For take-off, the pilot desires high lift with low drag to climb out over obstacles. To accomplish this, wing flaps are usually extended to one-fourth or one-half the flap travel. This permits additional lift to be obtained, but limits the drag. Beyond the half flap position, although it is true that wing flaps produce more lift with deflection, the drag increases to the extent that the flaps are acting more as air brakes than lifting devices. It is because of this braking effect, that more than one-half flap travel is not used in take-off or in operations where high lift with low drag is desired. For example, with the flaps in the retracted position while landing over obstacles, the airplane will require a long, shallow glide path which causes it to land at some point down the runway. With the air-brake effect of full flaps, however, the airplane descends at a much steeper angle. This permits landing closer to the approach end of the runway. The landing speed, with flaps, is slower when we touch down, and the airplane is easier to stop. In a retracted position, they are simply part of the lift-producing wing surface.

Today, airplanes are called *monoplanes* because they have only one wing on each side of the fuselage. In the older days there were biplanes—planes having two wings, one above the other. But this type of plane is today used only in special types of flying, because the two wings created too much added drag, and with high-powered power plants were no longer needed to provide extra lift.

THE POWER PLANT. The power plants used in most business and pleasure airplanes are fueled by gasoline, are air-cooled and are enclosed by a smooth, streamlined metal cover called a cowling (this corresponds to the "hood" on your automobile). Aside from design details, its main difference from an automobile engine is the propeller it rotates in order to "pull" the airplane forward. Aircraft engines are required by the Federal Aviation Agency to be inspected regularly to assure their safe performance.

"What," you may ask, "does one do if the airplane engine suddenly stops?" This is a perfectly reasonable question. Although they rarely do, airplane engines can, of course, stop . . . but don't panic. This in itself is hardly cause to become unduly concerned that the last will and testament is in perfect order. Concentrate, instead, on the principles of flight we have just discussed. The engine's function is to provide sufficient forward motion to create enough air moving over the wings to create lift. If the engine quits, sufficient forward speed can be achieved by putting gravity to work. We simply drop the nose of the airplane slightly down. The force of gravity will create a forward glide adequate to maintain forward motion, "thrust" or "flying speed" for surprisingly long distances. For example, the Cessna Skyhawk, illustrated in this book, has a 9.3 to 1 glide ratio. In other words, if you're one mile above the surface of the earth, you can glide 9.3 miles in any direction after the engine has stopped its operation. This means you have 271.7 square miles from which to select a landing location with the power off and at one mile of altitude. In addition, you would have about 11 minutes of flying time before the aircraft touched down on your selected landing spot.

Two questions that are often asked by would-be pilots are: Do I have to wear a parachute in a small aircraft? Are parachutes available aboard private planes? The answer to both is simply, *No!* And the reason is that they are not necessary, since the rate of descent of the average unpowered private aircraft is slower than an opened parachute. In addition, you have *full* control of the descent of a gliding plane. Thus, there's no need to ever abandon the airplane in flight and therefore, no need for parachutes carried aboard for this purpose.

THE EMPENNAGE. As the airplane is pulled through the air by the power plant, a method of providing stability and control is needed. This is accomplished by the empennage which consists of: vertical stabilizer, rudder, horizontal stabilizer and elevator.

The *vertical stabilizer* (that's the tall part of the tail) is often called "vertical fin." It's fixed and rigid. Its function is to provide directional stability (preventing the airplane from weaving and wobbling to the right or left) and to provide a mounting for the rudder.

The *rudder* moves right and left and is used (along *with* the ailerons) for making turns in the air. Here's how it works: When the rudder moves right, for instance, a low pressure area is created on the left side and a high pressure area on the right side. This causes the tail to move left and the nose of the airplane to turn right. The rudder is operated with the feet. For instance, when you push the right rudder pedal, the rudder swings right, forcing the tail to the left, which then swings the nose to the right. The left rudder pedal moves the rudder left and the airplane's nose to the right. The only place where the rudder does not work with the ailerons is in steering on the ground. There, like the rudder on a boat, it does the whole job aided in most new planes by the steerable nose wheel.

The *horizontal stabilizer* provides horizontal stability for the airplane (wouldn't you have guessed it!) and also provides a place to mount the elevators—and wouldn't you guess, too, that elevators on an airplane control the *up and down* attitude of the airplane—well, you're right, they do.

The *elevators* are movable metal flap-like extensions to the fixed horizontal stabilizer. They are operated by the control wheel (steering wheel) in the cabin. A gentle forward push on the control wheel forces them down. When this happens, the upper camber (shape) of the horizontal empennage (the surface including horizontal stabilizer and elevator) is increased creating a low pressure above—and a high pressure below the surfaces. This causes the tail of the airplane to move up and the nose to move down. Then the airplane starts descending. If you want to climb, you pull back on the control wheel. Then the opposite effect takes place—the tail of the airplane goes down and the nose goes up.

WHAT ABOUT THE INSTRUMENT PANEL?

As you can see, the basic art of flying involves the operation of *control surfaces*—that is, changing their camber or shape in order to vary the air pressures which can be used to control the altitude of the airplane. Like an automobile, an airplane has an ignition, a throttle (accelerator) and various instruments to tell how fast you're traveling, the operating condition of the engine and electrical system, etc. Since the airplane does operate in an extra dimension over an automobile, there are naturally some extra instruments and controls. Although these might look complicated at first, fledgling flyers soon learn that these instruments and controls are easy to check and use. Just as you don't keep your eyes glued to the instrument panel of your automobile—you don't keep your eyes on an aircraft instrument panel, either.

When looking at an aircraft instrument panel, you'll find one set of instruments that tells you what the plane is doing in level flight and maneuvers. A second set tells you the engine conditions. A third set consists of navigation instruments that help you find your way. The following are the specific instruments most generally found on a panel and what they do:

Turn and Bank Indicator. Shows you in a glance the rate of your turn and the smoothness with which you're executing it. It consists of a movable vertical needle and a metalball suspended in fluid in a curved glass tube. The needle and ball are deflected by movements of the aircraft.

Airspeed Indicator. Registers the indicated speed of the airplane through the air—miles per hour on outer gauge and universal nautical miles (knots) per hour on inner. It has green, yellow and red areas, indicating cruising, cautionary, and never-exceed speeds.

Altimeter. A form of barometer which measures atmospheric pressure, and registers this pressure in terms of altitude. When properly set, it will indicate the approximate height of the airplane above sea level. The height above an airport or the terrain immediately below can easily be ascertained. It is the difference between the altimeter reading and the known elevation of the airport or terrain as shown on the sectional aeronautical chart.

Rate-of-Climb Indicator. Tells how fast the airplane is climbing or descending in feet per minute. The indicator reads zero when the airplane is in level flight and is used to establish a certain rate of climb or descent.

Artificial Horizon (Gyro-Horizon). Tells you the plane's attitude relative to the real horizon. The dial shows a rear-view silhouette of an airplane and a horizontal line called the horizon bar. In level flight, the horizon bar stands directly behind the silhouette. When the plane climbs, the bar falls below the silhouette, just as the real horizon drops below your line of vision. When the plane glides, the bar rises above the silhouette. In a bank, the dial and the silhouette tilt with the plane, and the bar remains horizontal.

Magnetic Compass. Its primary function is to give direction in relation to the magnetic north pole.

Gyrocompass (Directional Gyro). Indispensable for instrument flying because it is steadier than the magnetic type. Settings are taken from magnetic compass during smooth flight, course is selected on scale of 5° intervals.

Ammeter, Fuel, Oil and Temperature Gauges. These give you the same type of information that similar gauges give you when driving an automobile. Most engine instruments and gauges are marked in colors to help you make quick and easy checks of engine performance. The markings indicate normal operating ranges and also minimum and maximum limits.

Tachometer. Indicates the rotational speed of an engine, usually in revolutions per minute, and gives you a general idea of the amount of power your engine is developing.

Suction Gauge. Most engines are equipped with a suction pump to operate the gyroscopic flight instruments. This gauge serves to inform the pilot as to the effectiveness of the suction system.

Clock. For recording take-off time, etc., and for timed turns in the air.

Not all the above instruments are found in every airplane—some have less, others have more. Also in recent years, airborne electronics have been vastly improved and have been added to the panel. Radios offer continuous and reliable use for both navigation and communication. Low-cost autopilots are available for private aircraft which make the pilot's job easier and safer. All single-engine airplanes can be equipped for safe flying during bad weather. Refinements such as Distance Measuring Equipment—which tells the pilot precisely how far he is from a ground radio station—are now available for private aircraft. More on electronic navigational aids can be found in Chapter Five.

Chapter 4

That First Flight

HAVING reached this point of the book, it is fairly safe to assume that you're really interested in learning to fly. So let's go out to the flight school of your choice and take that first flight . . . a big step toward the joys of flying your own airplane.

It was only a short time ago that I took my first lesson, so I know exactly how you feel. You're starting out on something entirely new. You're filled with eager anticipation. But, at the same time, there is a certain amount of that fear of the unknown that we all have. I all too well remember the first time I met my instructor, Pete Sarantis, at Mid-Island Air Service, and went aboard a Cessna 150 for my first lesson. As I sat there in the left seat (the pilot's seat), I'll confess, I had a few misgivings about my ability to learn to fly. Then I remembered how it was when my dad took driving lessons from the first automobile dealer in my home town. He was concerned, as I recall, about being too old to learn. But he did it because he knew he had to keep up with change. And learning to fly was *my* way of keeping up.

Pete, I must admit, was more like the golf pro at the club than the late night TV show concept of flight instructors. "Relax," he told me. "You won't be perfect—but you will be surprised at how good you really are!" Just listening to him perked up my confidence and made the whole business sound like fun!

Actually, the flight instructor's job is not only to help you work toward your private certificate, but to establish proper flight habits and get you started with the right attitude toward flying and learning. Of course, if there is a personality clash or you feel that a change of instructor might be beneficial to your progress, then discuss it with the director of the flight school and, if necessary, even change schools. But, if such problems should arise, take a good look at your own attitude before making such moves. Remember, that while teaching methods vary widely and each instructor's system will be largely his own, one thing holds true. Each has earned an instructor's certificate and, whoever he may be, his skill has met the approval of the Federal Aviation Agency. This flight instructor's certificate is just about the toughest to get in aviation, so listen and ask questions—you'll profit by it in more ways than one. Every pilot looks back with gratitude to an instructor (or instructors) who helped him over a particular obstacle, and you'll do the same.

It's a good idea, if you can arrange it, to plan to spend extra hours at the airport and listen. You can learn a lot more if don't limit yourself to going to the airport just at the scheduled periods. Many an instructor has cleared up landings (or other problems) for a student while the two of them were sitting in front of the airport office watching others. ("See, that student isn't getting set up correctly for landing—the nose should be higher." Or, "That's the way it should be, the nose is just right at touchdown and he's holding the wheel back as he should.") Unfortunately, the instructor in many cases gets paid only by the flight hour and has to schedule tightly in order to make a living, and such free time situations may be hard to come by.

PREFLIGHT INSPECTION
The first hour of your instruction starts with a preflight inspection. *All* pilots make this check before *each* flight. This inspection will vary with the size and com-

plexity of the airplane and the pilot usually refers to the airplane's owner manual regarding the items to be checked. But, by always beginning at a certain point and using an orderly procedure the inspection can be made systematically and will take only a few minutes. In the case of your first training flight, it may take a little longer because your instructor will explain the purpose and reasons for checking the various items.

As you look at the airplane you are about to fly in, you are bound to have some question again about the wisdom of your decision to learn to fly. I know I did after first looking at a business family plane close up. First, the engine in its nose was only about a quarter the size of my car's engine. But, what I didn't know was that, in spite of its compact size, the average aircraft engine develops a great deal more horsepower, pound for pound, than the auto type. Also many of the items under a car's hood that we usually consider part of the engine are not necessary in an airplane. For instance, an airplane doesn't require a radiator, water pump, and various hoses because its engine is air cooled. In addition, the lightness of the plane's construction gave me the impression that it was not sturdy enough to take me aloft. But, what I didn't know then—and possibly you don't now—is that the plane you're about to board is amazingly strong—actually more sturdily constructed than an airliner, in proportion to their respective weights and payloads.

THE TAKE-OFF

As you board the airplane, your instructor tells you to take the pilot's seat, while he takes the one at the right. (This side-by-side seating and dual control arrangement makes it easy for the student to understand the instructor, which gives you more confidence.) After adjusting your seat for comfort and fastening the seat belt, the instructor will explain the airplane's controls and instruments. You start the engine, check the instruments (per instructor's directions) and the plane is ready to taxi.

Taxiing the airplane is easy. You steer it on the ground with your feet on the rudder pedals which are connected to the nose wheel. To taxi the airplane you find that you're going to have to learn that "right" means to push with your right foot and "left" means to push with your left foot. There's a tendency by most beginning students to "overcontrol" the plane. The instructor explains that the controls are very responsive and advises a "soft touch."

"Always be gentle with the control," he tells you. "Treat the plane like a lady and she'll be good to you." Just before you reach the runway, you are directed to stop short of the run-up line. (In the plane you're "flying" the brakes are at the top of the rudder pedals.) Then you and your instructor "run through" the take-off check-list.

During this check the engine is "run-up" (accelerated). This is not just to warm it up, as you may think. It is done mainly to allow the pilot to check the magnetos which furnish electricity for the ignition system. Airplanes have a dual ignition system; that is, two magnetos, two spark plugs for each cylinder, etc. It is designed so that the engine will run on either one or both. Then, when the check-list is finished, you move out onto the runway after receiving a light or verbal instructions from the tower, or on an uncontrolled airport, after checking to see that both the runway and the approach to it are clear of other airplanes. It's important to remember that airplanes in the air have the right-of-way over those on the ground. When the sky is clear, you're instructed to taxi onto the runway and to swing around so that the craft heads *into* the wind. (Taking off against the wind decreases the distance required for take-off because you already have lift induced by the air flow over the wing; that is, you have airspeed before you start. The wind direction can be observed by visual indications such as wind socks or wind tees; at airports where there are control towers, this information may be received by radio.) If no other airplane is in front of

47

you on the runway or on its final landing approach, you're ready for take-off.

On your first lesson, the instructor then takes over and he pushes the throttle forward slowly until it's in the full-power position. With the engine on full, the airplane accelerates quickly and increases speed as it moves along the runway. (If the instructor should feel the plane pull to the left or right, he'll correct it with the rudder pedals.) As the plane accelerates, it reaches a speed at which it's ready to fly, which is shown by the airspeed indicator. (This speed is between 50 to 60 miles per hour in the type of plane you're in.) When this stage is reached, you'll actually feel that the airplane wants to fly. At this point, the instructor eases back slightly on the control wheel, the plane's nose moves up two or three inches, and the craft leaves the ground smoothly and surely.

Your instructor keeps holding the control wheel slightly back toward himself. By looking out of the plane's window you note that you're continuing to climb. The elevator in the tail is still raised. Shortly, you are several hundred feet in the air. You sit back now and relax, just enjoying the thrill of flying through the air, watching the ground slip by under you. Then, after a glance at the altimeter which reads 2,000 feet, you note that your instructor moves the control wheel forward slowly, so that it appears to be in a neutral position. The plane becomes level and does not rise any more. You're simply flying along through the clear, blue sky.

ME, FLY THE PLANE?

When the plane has leveled off, the instructor makes two simple adjustments. First he sets the throttle and locks it in that setting. It is never advisable to operate an engine at full power, except for the short time during take-off. Every plane manufacturer recommends the maximum revolutions per minute of his engine for continuous operation. This is called the *cruising rpm* of the engine. Your instructor has set the throttle so that the tachometer reads 2,300 rpms—the recommended cruising rating for the plane you're in. Normal cruising is done between 65% and 75% of full power.

The second adjustment he makes is to trim the plane so it will fly itself. On the elevator, there is a movable surface which is called a *trim tab*. You control it with a little wheel in the cabin, frequently located between both front seats. When you change the speed of an airplane, pressures on the control wheel change and you can adjust for it with the trim tab. Thus, when you're up in the air and your engine is at cruising speed, the plane should fly level. If it tends to want to climb or descend when the control wheel is released, the airplane can be made to fly level by adjusting this control. (This is called *trimming* the plane.) Roll the wheel ahead if the craft is tail heavy (wants to climb) and roll it back if the plane is nose heavy (wants to descend). Your instructor tells you that should you accidentally put the plane into an attitude from which you can't seem to recover to straight and level flight, just release the controls entirely, and the plane will automatically straighten itself out. The modern business family plane is designed with a built-in stability. It will always try to fly straight and level, especially once it has been properly trimmed. As a matter of fact, once these adjustments have been made flying becomes much easier than driving a car. In an automobile, you must keep moving the steering wheel almost continuously to keep properly located on your half of the highway, to turn corners and to pass slower traffic. Your eyes must watch the other automobiles, the highway, the road signs. In a plane, you set the hand throttle for a certain cruising speed and leave it there. Your flight path is usually straight to your destination; you have no need to turn, and you don't have to thread your way along a narrow highway.

During the first flight, your instructor will show you the practice area where you'll be doing most of your early flying and also will demonstrate the correct way to fly the traffic pattern around the airport. As you look out of the window at the ground below, you quickly discover that you're experiencing little or no sensation of height. The highways, vehicles and buildings below you appear Lilliputian in size but seem close enough for you to almost touch them. This is due to the fact that you have no perspective, no reference point by which you can judge your height. The dizziness that you may experience when looking down from atop of a tall building is because you see the sides of the other structures opposite from you to the street below and this makes you aware of how high you actually are. In the airplane, however, you see no such perspective or reference framework.

After you have had a chance to study the surrounding country from the air, your instructor demonstrates how the airplane reacts to the use of each control. You'll learn that the elevators don't "elevate" the craft—they are your airspeed control (point the nose down to speed up and vice versa for nose up)—and power (decrease or increase) is what makes an airplane glide or climb. Also you'll see that the rudder isn't used to turn the airplane in the air—that's the job of the ailerons, which bank the airplane. The rudder is used primarily as an aid to the ailerons to make smooth bank entries and roll-outs. After making a few turns, your instructor tells you to take over and make some.

It's easy. You don't have to turn an airplane; you simply bank it. This is done by simply turning the control wheel. But neater turns can be made by coordinating the rudder pedals with the control wheel. For example, to make a 90° left turn, the control wheel is turned to the left and the left rudder pedal is simultaneously pressed until the plane goes into a normal bank. Then the controls are neutralized, except for holding a little back pressure on the control wheel to keep the nose from dipping, and the plane will remain in the turn. When it is time to straighten out the airplane, it is "rolled out" simply by turning the control wheel to the right and pressing the right rudder pedal. It's often been said: Don't try to turn an airplane —gently roll it in whichever direction you wish to take.

While aloft on your first flight, there may be some physical sensations that may cause you little concern, but these are due to the fact that flying is new to you. When on the ground you travel in only two dimensions; when flying, you move in a third—vertically. While an elevator moves vertically, it has no forward and sideways motion. The combinations of these three movements in flight give your inner ear, which controls your sense of balance, a certain degree of discomfort, but usually *only* until you become accustomed to them. The first time your instructor banks the airplane in a turn you might have a strange feeling and, to complicate your problems even more, you lean your body to the opposite side in a subconscious effort to keep from falling out. But remember that he banks the plane in a turn for the same reason you lean a bicycle over when you go around a corner. Thus, you should allow yourself to bank with the plane in the same manner as you do on a bike. There is no danger whatsoever of falling out of the plane's cabin; the doors are almost impossible to open wide against the outside slipstream of air. The seat belt, which is fastened across your lap, is not intended to keep you from falling out; it is to keep you firmly in your seat.

Your instructor will also mention the various visual flight regulations (VFR) such as when two planes should meet on the same course, they alter their courses to pass one another on the right. A plane overtaking a slower one passes it on the right. When two planes cross courses, the one having the other on its left has the right of way. And every airport has a traffic pattern for incoming and outgoing planes. But, as you thrill at handling an airplane and ponder the many things the instructor has told you, your first hour of flight is over. The instructor permits you to fly back to the airport. Then he lands the plane, explaining each step as he does it. Landing an airplane seems simple and easy, too.

LANDING

When the airplane is about two-thirds down the "down-wind leg" (flying with the wind, parallel to the runway), your instructor runs through the brief landing check-list and eases back on the power. From then on the airplane is in a glide. Just past the end of the runway the plane makes a 90° left turn into the "base leg" and then is turned left again to line up with the runway for the "final approach," which is into the wind.

One thing you are told to remember about the landing approach is to keep your eyes ahead of you, looking down the runway (about the same distance ahead as driving a car at comparable speed). When the time comes to level off, you *feel* it. There are three basic steps to landing . . . but they blend into one smooth movement of the control wheel. The first is the normal glide; then at a proper distance from the ground, the control wheel is eased back to flatten the glide; then eased back more to lift the nose of the airplane. The knack is to hold the plane just off the ground as long as you can. As the plane loses speed it will settle to the ground and all that must be done is to steer with the pedals and apply the brakes if necessary. After the airplane has been landed, you'll be issued a regulation flight log in which your first flight lesson is entered . . . a permanent record that is yours to keep and add to!

After my first flight lesson, as I walked to the hangar, I felt like a new man . . . and I was! Like anyone who has learned something new, I felt bigger for the experience. In only two hours I actually learned why an airplane flies, how it flies—and I had even handled one myself. I couldn't help thinking about how easy it had been to make this change in my life, once I had made up my mind to do it. As I looked ahead a little to the ways this flying busi-

Coming in for a landing at Logan Airport, Boston.

ness would change things for me, I was glad I had made the decision.

Chapter 5

Obtaining Your Private
Pilot License

AFTER your first flight, you're ready for the serious fun of obtaining your private pilot certificate. Your flight training can be broken down into three basic categories: presolo, solo and post-solo.

In this book, we're not going to give instructional steps on any of these categories. Your flight instructor will do this much better than we could ever hope. But, since the purpose of the book is to give you some idea as to the *joys of flying your own airplane,* this chapter is devoted to highlighting the major points of flight training as they pertain to a private pilot license.

THE FOUR FUNDAMENTALS

Your first few lessons will be devoted to making you feel at ease in the airplane and learning the four fundamentals—straight and level flight, turns, climbs, and glides.

1. *Straight and Level Flight:*

Straight flight involves direction while level flight means the maintaining of a constant attitude. Thus, your role in straight and level flight is to restore the airplane to its proper heading and attitude if it's deflected from either. Level flight, at first, is a matter of consciously fixing the relationship of the position of some portion of the airplane, used as a reference point, with the horizon. As experience is gained, these mechanical aids give away more or less to a "sense" of being level, but these same mechanical aids are still used as checks throughout your pilot career. With the exception of the special instruments used in instrument flying, they are the only known method of accurately and instantly judging the attitude of the plane. (The term *attitude* must not be confused with the word *altitude*. Attitude refers to the position of the airplane in relation to the ground, such as the position of the nose above or below the horizon, or the angle at which the airplane is banked. Altitude, of course, means the height of the airplane above the ground.)

Level flight is when the nose and tail are at the same altitude. It is usually accomplished by using some portion of the nose as a reference point, usually a spot on the cowl, and keeping this point in a fixed position relative to the horizon. In addition, level flight involves keeping the wings level and it is accomplished by visually checking the relationship of the tips of the wings with the horizon. Straight-and-level flight requires little or no pressure on the controls if the airplane is properly trimmed. But, you must learn to know when corrections are necessary and then make them by using your reference points.

2. *Turns:*

On your first flight, you made several turns to get the feeling of the controls. As you continue your lessons, you'll learn to confine your turns to three kinds of banks: shallow, medium, and steep. In the average instructional airplane at cruising speed, shallow turns generally involve banks from the least perceptible to about 15°; medium turns at 15° to 25°; and steep turns begin at about 25°.

The medium bank is usually chosen for initial instruction in turns because it's the easiest to perform. It is also the only bank that will remain constant when controls are released. In other words, pressure on the controls is required to maintain both shallow and steep banks. Your

56

instructor will take you through the various banks and you will be able to determine the amount of pressure required for these turns.

3. *Climbs:*

Climbing is the procedure used to ascend from one level to another, and then, when the desired height has been reached, to resume level flight. To make the actual climb, the nose is eased up to the proper position relative to the horizon and the throttle is opened smoothly to the recommended climb power so that the best rate of climb is maintained. While first learning the climbing process, you'll resort to some mechanical means, such as the position of some reference point on the nose in relation to the horizon, for angle, and an airspeed indicator for speed. As time goes by, you'll be able to coordinate the use of the throttle to the degree of climb desired.

4. *Glides:*

A gliding airplane, which is flight without engine power, differs from a plane in powered flight only in that it must inevitably follow a downward flight path. During a glide, an airplane can be maneuvered just as it can be during powered flight. It's not out of control, nor will it "fall out of the sky" as is sometimes quoted in newspapers, simply because the engine is idling or completely stopped.

In gliding flight the engine is throttled and the power to propel the airplane forward is supplied by gravity. The airplane acts about the same as a sled when coasting down a hill: The steeper the hill the faster the sled will go. You have the advantage of being able to vary the steepness of the imaginary hill down which the airplane is gliding and thus to control your forward speed.

A *straight glide* is just as simple as straight flying and is done as follows: Close the throttle gradually, allowing the engine to idle. Lower the nose far enough below the horizon to maintain normal gliding speed. Trim the airplane with the adjustable trim tab control wheel so that the nose stays in the lowered position without either forward or backward pressure on the control wheel.

When throttling the power for a glidé, the carburetor heat control should be pulled out, since the carburetor may ice up when engine power is drastically reduced. This is especially true when the temperature is between 20° and 70° F., and when there is visible moisture or high humidity present. The carburetor heater is an anti-icing device which preheats the air before it reaches the carburetor and thus keeps moisture from forming into ice.

PRESOLO FLIGHT MANEUVERS

Flight maneuvers will be introduced by your instructor in order of difficulty and you'll be allowed time to absorb and handle each new situation before moving on. Your first maneuvers will generally be combinations of the four fundamentals such as climbing and gliding turns, etc.

One of the first maneuvers you'll be introduced to is the S-turn. The simplest type of S-turn consists of banking the airplane to a medium bank and maintaining this bank until a turn of 180° has been completed. The bank is then reversed, and a turn of 180° is made in the opposite direction. Continuing this procedure—reversing the turn every 180°—causes the airplane to fly in a continuous S pattern over the ground. Later shallow and steep banked S-turns will be practiced.

As part of your presolo work you'll do wind drift correction maneuvers such as the rectangular course and S-turns across a road. The former consists of flying a pattern around a rectangular field at a comparatively low, but safe, altitude, correcting for the effects of crosswinds, which tend to "drift" the airplane off course. The S-turn is a series of semicircles flown across a road that is perpendicular to the wind, and you'll learn that you can correct for wind drift effects while flying along a curved path. Both of these maneuvers are designed to teach the fundamentals of drift corrections as well as getting you accustomed to flying the airplane with your attention directed outside.

In your presolo days, you will practice some stalls. As you spend time around the airport you will hear about stalls—mostly to avoid them—so you are probably quite curious as to what they are all about. If you're expecting something exciting, I'm afraid you'll be a little disappointed, for there won't be a great deal of sensation from a stall. As a matter of fact, an airplane, once forced into a stall condition, can recover of its own accord without any help from you.

Actually, the word "stall" causes a great deal of confusion. This word is a common one to anyone who drives a car. It is commonly used by pilots, too, but when they say "stall" they mean something else. In motorists' lingo, when your car "stalls" the engine stops. In the language of flying, however, a "stall" is a maneuver of the airplane—and has absolutely nothing to do with whether the engine is still working. It is really the condition of an airplane when it has lost the speed necessary for level flight, or for maintaining a constant altitude. It is caused by climbing too steeply, gliding too flat, turning too sharply, or by any other maneuver which results in a loss of speed. (Almost all planes are equipped with a stall warning device or horn which sounds an aural warning between 5 and 10 mph above the stall speed of the craft. Such a device warns the pilot of an approaching stall.) For instance, one of the easiest ways to cause a stall is to raise the nose (pull back on the control wheel) without adding power. This is similar to trying to climb a hill in a car without adding power. Like the car, your airplane will lose speed. Whereas the car will eventually stop and then begin to roll back down the hill, the airplane, which has no road to hold it up, will nose down of its own accord. All you have to do to correct the stall condition is to let the control wheel go *slightly* forward, keeping the nose down to let the speed pick up to where it should be (like going down the other side of the hill in an automobile)—and you will soon be flying level again.

Stalls can be done with or without power (the engine at idle) and serve as the next step to moving on to landing practice. You'll also practice "slow flight" (flying the airplane at minimum airspeeds, which will help you recognize an approaching stall and to establish precise airspeed and altitude control habits).

The usual routine for take-offs and landings during the presolo phase is to introduce them gradually, followed by nearly the full flight being taken up by these maneuvers in the latter stages. Probably you will be making take-offs yourself after the first flight or so and will gradually ease into landing later.

While there are right-turn traffic patterns at some airports, the standard pattern most generally employed is a rectangular course flown with left-hand turns. Like any rectangle, the traffic pattern has four sides or "legs" each of which is given a name. The first leg is the *take-off leg*. Generally, on the take-off leg, you maintain straight climbing flight until you're about 400 to 600 feet above the earth. Then you make your first turn to the left. This turn can be either a level turn or a climbing turn, depending on the local airport procedure.

The *crosswind leg* is also a climbing leg. If you intend to remain in the pattern, the crosswind leg is usually flown for as long as is needed to climb 200 feet. In the event that you wish to leave traffic pattern, you can do so from the cross-wind leg by making a 45° turn to the right. This leg, which is not in the rectangular pattern, is called the *exit leg,* and it is also a climbing leg. But the exit leg doesn't have to be flown during the dual flights just preceeding solo, or for several solo flights afterward. This is due to the fact that during this period, you shoot "touch-and-go" landings, which means that you circle the field without leaving the traffic pattern. Thus, on the crosswind leg, you turn left again, still climbing during the turn so as to emerge from both the turn and the climb at the "pat-

60

tern altitude" prescribed for the airport. And, of course, having turned, you have entered another leg.

This is the *downwind leg*, which can be considered a level flight leg. It is flown downwind, as its name implies, from 1/2 to 3/4 of a mile away from the runway. Downwind flight, as you remembered from your first flight, is opposite to the direction in which you intend to land. On this leg you make several important decisions. You select your "spot" for landing. In the event you intend to land power off, you apply carburetor heat, go through your landing check list, close the throttle and establish your glide. Then all that remains is the *base leg*, which is a gliding leg, and the *final approach*, which is usually the same runway used for the take-off leg.

Like most students, you'll have an inflated idea of the importance of landings as compared to the other maneuvers. Landings *are* important—very important—but so are the other skills you must learn. It may seem during early landing practice that you have no idea where the ground is; you'll want to level off too high or may tend to touch down (land) before you are quite ready. Then one day things fall into place and you know where the ground is. That is when progress picks up. You won't always make perfect landings (who does?) and will be shown what to do in case you bounce or level-off too high. Getting ready to solo does not mean flying perfectly, but hinges mostly on your judgment and your ability to recognize and *correct* your errors. Remember that you must keep a careful record of all your flight time in your logbook.

ME SOLO?

One day you'll be shooting take-offs and landings and, as you taxi back to the take-off end of the runway, the instructor will say casually, "Okay, you take it around and shoot a landing. I'll be standing right here, so taxi back when you're done." You'll taxi out, line up and take off as you've done many times before—but this time you are *alone* . . . wonderfully alone. The right seat, strangely empty for the first time, takes on a new significance, a mute symbol of self-reliance. The expected feeling of fear at being alone fails to materialize as the ground rushes by and then drops slowly away. The horizon dips out of sight and the beckoning sky ahead seems to welcome this latest intrusion on its privacy.

Hold slight pressure on the right rudder to keep the plane tracking straight ahead. Pass the end of the field no more than 400 feet above the surface, keeping the runway right behind the tail. Climb on out for another half-mile before leveling off for a left turn.

Eight long flying hours ago, the thought of soloing was a distant dream, a fantasy in which you projected yourself into an impossible role, like a child substituting himself for Willie Mays. But now you can touch the dream—just as you can touch the machine which has transported you into it.

Check for other traffic in the pattern. Bank left. Don't rush the turn. Let it come around smoothly and roll out with the nose at a slight angle to the right to compensate for wind.

Eight hours ago. Three weeks by the calendar. Then, an airplane was just a confusion of parts, gauges, handles, lights, and pointers that went round and round or up and down for no apparent reason. The inscrutable face of the instrument panel stared mockingly back, daring you to decipher its messages. On your very first lesson, you timidly stepped into the pilot's seat and, at the instructor's patient bidding, brought the engine roaring to life and felt a gentle shudder sweep through the craft. Your early hours together with this new friend were filled with experiments as man and machine tested and probed and poked at each other, feeling for strengths and weaknesses, seeking mutual understanding, giving and forgiving. You often felt the airplane had a will of its own, like a large animal leading you on a leash while you anxiously tried to guess its next move.

Gain more altitude before turning left onto the down-

wind leg. Take a quick look at the panel. Pull the throttle back a little more. Watch that altimeter. Level off at 800 feet above the ground.

Gradually, though, you began to understand, and the airplane responded to your will, not its own. The needles no longer moved in mysterious orbit. The gauges spoke to you in plain language. You led the animal, rather than trailing meekly behind. The calm voice of reason displaced doubt. And then one day the instructor pushed back his seat and calmly folded his arms while you were on final approach. So soon? You tightened your grip on the control wheel and throttle and somehow completed the landing. The airplane tugged to the right on touchdown and the nose wheel came down too hard and you ballooned back into the air briefly—but you had landed all by yourself. Your palms were strangely damp and you attempted a smile as you wiped them on your pant legs, wondering if the instructor could see through your false front. Of course, most instructors don't tell you beforehand when you will solo. For one reason, should you hit a slump during the period indicated for solo and the instructor has to spend more time with you, it's bad for morale.

Continue downwind, checking again for other traffic. Pull on the carburetor heat when the airplane is opposite the desired landing point on the runway. Reduce power and hold the airspeed to 80 mph. Turn left onto base leg and set up a glide path to the end of the runway.

And then more practice. And more. Until finally today you're on your own, sent on your way with a final quip from the instructor as he stepped slowly from the airplane and methodically formed a large "X" with the safety belt straps by crossing them on his seat—the empty seat which now almost cries out for attention. A corny thought comes to mind. "X" marks the spot where your morale used to sit. And then it strikes you. This is what you've wanted all along. This is why you got involved in the first place. Somewhere inside, you had been seeking an experience like this. Now, for the first time, you see beyond the panel and the wingtips and the runway growing larger on your left. You feel suddenly relaxed.

Turn onto final approach. Reduce power some more and aim for the numbers at the end of the runway. Everything's going fine. Keep it tracking down the center line of the runway. Landing coming up.

You are flying! The distant dream, the untouchable fantasy of not long ago, is now reality. You feel a new dimension in personal satisfaction—a feeling of self-reliance that springs from conquering doubt and stepping up to a new challenge.

Pull the power off. Flare out. Back on the wheel . . . pull it on back . . . back. Let the airplane settle. Runway coming up. Easy, now. Keep it level with the runway . . . let it come on down. Touchdown! Smooth . . . I have SOLOED!

Reason says that countless others before you have gone through this experience, but pride still wells up. It doesn't take long for the word to spread and soon you're deluged with enthusiastic congratulations and handshakes, many of which are from other student pilots who are also looking forward to their big day. The first solo is almost, without exception, surrounded by traditional rituals such as the "shirt-tail clipping" ceremony. The piece of cloth thus obtained is generally inscribed with the student's name, the date and the instructor's signature. Many schools give students special solo trophies on which the autographed shirt-tail clipping may be mounted. But the big thrill remains in your own mind, which is already beginning to relive deliciously those last few minutes in the air that will never again be duplicated—nor forgotten.

POST-SOLO MANEUVERS

For most new pilots, the solo is the end of the world, but to your instructor, it's a minor milestone—a psychological barrier out of the way. You have received an *endorsement* on your student license, proof that your instructor feels you are a good enough flier to go up by yourself. (As a student, you must have such an endorsement for each make and model of aircraft you fly, after your instructor has determined that you can fly it.) Most new pilots get through solo mechanically, but after solo your instructor wants to see a real awareness building. Before solo you worked on basics; in this stage you will be introduced to more precise flying that will include advanced stalls, 720-degree turns around a point on the ground (a wind drift correction maneuver similar in theory to the S-turns across a road that consists of flying two complete turns of a constant radius about a point on the ground, correcting for the wind by varying the bank), short and soft-field take-off and landing techniques, gusty wind take-offs and landings and general smoothing out of the basic maneuvers.

During your advanced training, you'll be instructed on how to meet an emergency and how to respond to it. For example, you'll learn about forced landing. This type of landing becomes necessary in the event of complete loss of engine power—and the odds of this occurring are about the same as your winning the Irish Sweepstakes. The aim, however, in practicing forced landing approaches is to make you so familiar with the procedure, that should an actual engine failure occur, you won't waste time wondering what to do and how to plan an approach. The proper and immediate procedure should become second nature to you. As a matter of fact, forced landings are essentially one of the simplest maneuvers taught in flying. There's nothing about them that is any different from a normal airfield landing except that they are less complicated. You don't have to consider airport traffic patterns or other planes, and as a rule, the forced landing can be made in virtually any direction, even upwind or crosswind. (Such wind direction indications as smoke from chimneys, waves on the water, and the appearance of the foliage on trees are easily observed from the air.) In most cases, the forced landing fields are larger than the space available for landing on an airport. Thus in almost every example, forced landings are easier to execute than an airport one, once the student has caught the trick, but in almost every instance, they remain a stumbling block. Not because they're difficult, but because most students persist in thinking they are. In other words, forced landings, real or simulated, are completely a matter of mental hazard—and the best way to remove this hazard is by practicing forced landing approaches.

Although the modern airplane, with proper maintenance, is the most trouble free of any transporting vehicle, there's still the very remote possibility that an emergency might develop while in flight. The most important thing to remember in an emergency is *not* to panic. Remain as calm as possible and try to determine the best course of action. If a situation develops when you're uncertain as to your position or feel apprehensive for your safety, don't hesitate to request assistance by radio. You're never alone when you're in the air.

In your pre-private license days, you'll be introduced to instrument (or blind) flying. While there is *no* required number of hours for this training for the private certificate, most flight schools offer at least five hours of instrument instruction. You'll be expected to do simple maneuvers under "blind" conditions on the private flight test. The reasoning behind this requirement is mainly to prepare you to turn back safely in case you someday run into a cloud or encounter zero visibility and lose sight of your ground reference.

Training in instrument flying means, as a rule, donning the plastic mask (a bit like an anteater's beak) which blocks out everything but the view of the panel itself, as your instructor takes you through various blind maneuvers. First off, you must just keep the plane straight and level. Then climbs, descents, and holding maneuvers all begin to seem feasible without reference to anything outside the cabin. Of course, whether you have gotten where you wanted to go depends upon whether you consulted all the necessary instruments, and in the necessary order that works whether you're flying straight, descending, banking, or whatever.

You will notice that we haven't said anything about spins. Many years ago a spin, or "tailspin" as it was then called, was regarded as an extremely dangerous maneuver because recovery was almost impossible. Today, however, only a very few modern general aviation planes are *capable* of spinning and these are designed and tested to recover from spins even *without the aid of the pilot*. Actually, to spin a newer business family aircraft is a *forced* and *difficult* maneuver to make a plane do even when the pilot so desires. Spins are so rare today that learning to recover from one is not even required for your private license.

CROSS-COUNTRY

The cross-country aeronautical experience requirement for the private certificate calls for at least ten hours of solo cross-country, including a landing at a place at least 25 miles from the point of departure and at least one flight including a landing at a location more than 100 miles from the point of departure. Actually your cross-country flights are one of the most interesting phases of your training. You'll begin to see how the airplane is intended to be used—as a safe and efficient means of transportation. In other words, you'll soon be agreeing with us when we say that the private plane is the best way to get from one place to another. And as you travel the highways of the sky, you'll find a courtesy and obedience of rules and regulations that is unheard of on land roads.

Most cross-country flights in the early days of aviation were done mostly by pilotage, which meant flying from one landmark to another with visual reference to the ground. Many early pilots would follow a highway or railroad from one city to another. Today aerial navigation is much safer and easier for the pilot who has a good knowledge of the fundamentals. The Federal Aviation Agency and various private concerns have done much to aid in making navigation easier and safer. Among these aids are:

Flight Service Stations (FSS) operated by the FAA are continually at the service of any pilot. These stations accept flight plans filed by the pilot, broadcast current weather twice each hour for the convenience of airborne pilots, and may be contacted any time for flight, airport and weather information. A special feature of the stations is *Flight Following Service* (FFS) available to any pilot upon request, under which the network of ground radio stations will set up a "watch" on the airplane from the time it takes off until it lands at its destination.

Weather briefings are available at almost any airport which give current weather conditions at hundreds of places around the country. Weather forecasts will also give a reasonably accurate picture of what conditions will be at any place within the next few hours. Of course, there's no mode of conveyance which is completely weatherproof. (Weather conditions and movements are checked by the pilot with the weather service of the FAA or Weather Bureau before take-off, but experience dictates that he will often check en route as well.) If extreme conditions exist, the FAA Flight Service Station will give the pilot a detour routing so as to miss the storm.

Radio navigational aids are almost always within range of the airplane. These make it possible to navigate almost any place in the country using only the radio for directional reference. Modern radio navigation systems have replaced annoying headsets and aural signals with easy-to-read visual presentations on the instrument panel. More on radio navigational aids can be found on page 77.

Detailed maps, or aeronautical charts, of the entire country, showing all towns and cities, railroads, major roads, rivers, prominent landmarks, etc., are available to all pilots for use in navigation. The FAA also issues various publications which are of considerable value to a pilot The best known and most valuable of these publications is the *Airman's Information Manual*. This manual contains the listing of facilities at airports, radio communications and navigational aids, new and changing control areas, and much additional information helpful to the pilot. While a copy is available to pilots at all Flight Service Stations, it is recommended that once you get your license (or even before) you subscribe to this publication because it supplements the aeronautical charts and keeps you up to date on the latest flight information. For complete data on aeronautical charts, the *Airman's Information Manual,* and other FAA publications, write to the Superintendent of Documents, United States Government Printing Office, Washington, D. C. 20025 or check at your local airport.

Procedures for cross-country flight training vary between flight schools, but the usual approach for the first dual flight is a triangular route to two strange airports. This first trip consists of comparatively short legs during which the instructor will double-check your ability to fly by pilotage using aeronautical charts. As previously stated, these are a series of detailed sectional charts covering most of the continent, ground maps with a scale of eight miles to the inch and each including an area of about 300 by 150 miles, and are brought up to date about every six months. These show, as previously stated, the topography of the area, airports, railroads, high-tension lines— everything to aid the pilot in his navigation—and also tall obstacles that might be a hazard to low flying—and, of course, the airways and radio aids to navigation. World aeronautical charts (WACs) cover about four times the area and are less detailed. Private agencies supply detailed diagrams of almost every airport in the country.

Before your first, short cross-country flight, the instructor spreads out a chart, which includes both your airport and the one you plan to visit, on a big table. With a pencil and ruler, he draws a line from one field to the other. This line is your course. After he folds the chart so that your course and the land on either side of it are easy to see, the instructor hands it to you to study. He suggests that you list the landmarks you should see along the course in a notebook in the same order as you expect to pass them.

After checking the weather report for the area between two airports and finding that the weather is favorable along the entire course, you're ready for take-off. Once aloft, you notice your first guide—a broad superhighway. It's going in the same direction as you wish to go, but it is to one side of your course. You maneuver your plane so that the highway appears as if it were just off your left wing tip. After you have flown along beside it for about ten miles, the highway turns off to the left, while your course continues straight ahead. Checking your notes, the next landmark is a tall smokestack, ten miles ahead. Before the road has disappeared behind you, the stack is spotted on the horizon.

The next guide point is a small town four miles farther on. It's almost square, with an outdoor theatre on one corner and large oil tank on another. From the town you follow your course along a single-track railroad. Then, finally, you come into sight of the town where you want to land. It's not difficult to know you're at your destination because the chart has shown that it is an L-shaped town built along the banks of a river. On approaching the town you note an air marker on top of the dark roof of a large building. This marker has the name of the town painted in large yellow letters; an arrow shows the direction and distance to the airport. In a minute or so you see the airport and land the plane. You have completed your first cross-country flight.

Most cross-country flights are just as simple as the one just described, but they all require planning. To compute direction and distance from a known position, you must consider altitude to be flown, airport temperature, distance to be covered, compass variation and deviation, wind direction and velocity, and gallons of gas per hour your plane will consume. Although it is possible to fly an airplane cross-country and calculate all the information required by the use of arithmetic and trigonometry, it's much easier to do the figuring with the aid of a computer. There are several types of computers available, but your instructor will help you to choose the best one for you and will show how it should be used.

On cross-country flight covering a considerable distance, you can obtain the free safety aid called *Flight Following Service*. This involves filing a flight plan with one of the over 800 FAA Flight Service Stations, many of which can be contacted by direct telephone from the airport. The flight plan includes your route, the time you expect to be over certain definite checkpoints, and your time of arrival at your destination. Your plan is transmitted by teletype to the flight service stations along your course, and you report by radio when you pass near them, and also when you land at your destination. At each check, you are informed of weather changes ahead of you. By this Flight Following Service, the ground personnel of the FAA know where you are at all times.

RADIO COMMUNICATION

Until recent years, many pilots relied entirely upon pilotage when making cross-country flights. Today, radio navigational aids and communications facilities play a major part in these flights. Actually these electronic aids are one of the major reasons for the boom in general aviation. They permit the business pleasure pilot to fly cross-country with ease and skill of his airline brethren.

At the busy airports throughout the country, arriving and departing air traffic is directed by control towers. Although light-gun signals are sometimes used when small airplanes are not radio-equipped, most airport traffic control instructions are given by radio. Two-way radio communication is *required* for all aircraft taking off or landing at an airport at which an FAA-operated control tower is located unless prior authorization is obtained from the tower. Also on cross-country flights many situations arise which make it desirable to use two-way radio while en route. For example, a pilot may wish to obtain information concerning current weather along his course or the airport conditions at his destination. Such information may be readily obtained by using the radio to call the nearest FAA Flight Service Station.

The frequencies of radio range stations and radio beacons having voice facilities are used for air-ground communications purposes and for aviation weather broadcasts. These broadcasts are based upon weather observations made each hour throughout the United States. Weather broadcasts are made twice hourly. An airway broadcast is made at 45 minutes past the hour and consists of weather reports from important terminals located on airways within approximately 400 miles of the broadcasting station. An area broadcast is made at 15 minutes past the hour and consists of reports from stations within approximately 150 miles of the broadcasting station.

Some inexperienced pilots are reluctant to use radio navigational aids and communications facilities because they are not familiar with phraseologies, air traffic control procedures, and the conveniences of radio aids to navigation. However, private pilots can no longer afford to overlook the advantages and safety features which are available through use of radio. True, the FAA recommends and good operating practice demands that pilots use their two-way radios for airground communications. For instance, when ready to transmit, you should hold the microphone close to your mouth. After giving thought to what you're going to say, you should speak in a normal tone of voice. Although the message may be phrased in your own words, certain radiotelephone phraseologies are commonly used in order to reduce the length of transmissions to a minimum and to provide uniformity. The following are a few of these phraseologies:

Word or Phrase	*Meaning*
ACKNOWLEDGE	"Let me know that you have received and understand this message."

72

ROGER	"I have received all of your last transmission." (It is used to acknowledge receipt, and shouldn't be used for other purposes.)
AFFIRMATIVE	"Yes."
NEGATIVE	"That is not correct."
I SAY AGAIN	Self-explanatory.
SAY AGAIN	Self-explanatory.
STAND BY	Self-explanatory.
VERIFY	"Check with originator."
OVER	"My transmission is ended and I expect a response from you."
OUT	"This conversation is ended; I do not expect a response from you."
CORRECTION	"An error has been made in this transmission (or message indicated)."

To illustrate two-way communications procedures, let's make a flight from Abilene Municipal Airport, Abilene, Texas, to Love Field, Dallas, Texas, flying direct. First, you go in person to the Weather Bureau Airport Service to check the weather. Next, you file a VFR Flight Plan via interphone with the Abilene Flight Service Station. After completing all preparations for the flight, you call the control tower giving the following information: Aircraft identification, position, the type of operation planned (under visual flight regulations [VFR] or instrument [IFR]), and the point of first intended landing. For example:

You: ABILENE TOWER THIS IS CESSNA FIVE ONE ZERO TWO BRAVO (Cessna N5102B) AT HANGAR TWO, READY TO TAXI, VFR FLIGHT TO DALLAS, OVER.

Tower: CESSNA ZERO TWO BRAVO, CLEARED TO RUNWAY ONE FOUR. WIND SOUTHEAST ONE SIX (16 nautical miles per hour). ALTIMETER TWO NINE NINE EIGHT. TIME ZERO EIGHT THREE ONE (8:31 A. M.)
You: CESSNA ZERO TWO BRAVO, ROGER

After taxiing to runup position on the taxi strip and completing your pre-take-off checklist, you call the tower:

You: ABILENE TOWER CESSNA ZERO TWO BRAVO, READY FOR TAKE-OFF.

The tower controller determines that there's no conflicting traffic and replies:

Tower: CESSNA ZERO TWO BRAVO, CLEARED FOR TAKE-OFF.
You: CESSNA ZERO TWO BRAVO, ROGER.

You continue to guard the control tower frequency until leaving the control zone, or until cleared to leave the tower frequency. While proceeding along the airway, you give a position report to the FAA Flight Service Station at Mineral Wells, and ask for the latest weather information at Dallas. You first establish contact with Mineral Wells, indicating the frequency on which a reply is expected.

You: MINERAL WELLS RADIO THIS IS CESSNA FIVE ONE ZERO TWO BRAVO. REPLY ON ONE TWENTY-TWO POINT TWO MEGACYCLES. OVER.
Station: CESSNA FIVE ONE ZERO TWO BRAVO THIS IS MINERAL WELLS RADIO. OVER.
You: Then proceed with your message: ZERO TWO BRAVO SIX MILES WEST OF MINERAL WELLS AT FIVE THOUSAND FIVE HUNDRED ON VFR FLIGHT PLAN ABILENE TO DAL-

LAS. REQUEST LATEST DALLAS WEATHER. OVER.

Station: Mineral Wells Radio complies by furnishing latest weather reports.

You: CESSNA ZERO TWO BRAVO, ROGER. OUT.

While in the vicinity of Fort Worth, you might wish to contact Fort Worth Radio for further information. When approximately 15 miles west of Dallas, you call the tower at Love Field. This type of message usually includes the following items: Position, time (optional), flight altitude, request for information or clearance—if pertinent.

You: LOVE TOWER THIS IS CESSNA FIVE ONE ZERO TWO BRAVO, ONE FIVE MILES WEST, FOUR TWO, THREE THOUSAND. REQUEST LANDING INSTRUCTIONS. OVER.

Tower: CESSNA FIVE ONE ZERO TWO BRAVO, ONE FIVE MILES WEST, AT FOUR TWO, CLEARED TO ENTER TRAFFIC PATTERN, RUNWAY THREE SIX, LEFT TURNS. WIND NORTH-NORTHWEST ONE FIVE. OVER.

You then enter the traffic pattern on the downwind leg, and report to the tower while turning on base leg. After receiving a clearance to land, you acknowledge and proceed with your landing. While turning off the active runway, the tower instructs you to tune to ground control frequency for further taxi instructions. You proceed to the parking area, continuing to monitor the ground control frequency until the airplane is parked.

You close your flight plan by telephone with the Flight Service Station as soon after landing as possible. Another suggested method of closing a flight plan would be to contact the Flight Service Station prior to entering the airport traffic area and close it by radio. Another method of closing a flight plan is by radio with the tower after landing. Federal Aviation Regulations permit this but it's not generally recommended due to the added congestion on already overcrowded control tower communications frequencies. It's for this reason that the method of closing by telephone is recommended.

In all cases the conversations are informal but to the point in the jargon of aircraft radio. Though the traffic tower operator and you may never meet, the camaraderie is quite like that of men who daily work side by side. Through this kinship of the air you are never "alone" as is the man who drives through a region all by himself in an automobile.

A notable courtesy among pilots in the air is radio relay. Sometimes you may wish to contact a control center somewhat distant and for one reason or another don't get through right away. Pilots of other aircraft closer to that control center will relay the conversation if they don't hear the original call answered.

In World War II combat flying, a fighter pilot would tip off his buddy that an enemy was bearing down on him with "Bogey at 10 o'clock." This would place the position of the on-coming aircraft in terms of the hands of the clock, as if the pilot were in the pivot of the clock's hands. This courtesy has peaceful application in the control centers where position and movement of aircraft are followed on radar scanners. The pilots get frequent calls en route stating, "traffic two miles, moving south at two o'clock" (or whatever the actual position).

How does the control center know who is who? There are numerous ways. On instrument flight plans it is a simple matter because control center literally follows on radar the aircraft progress from take-off. Unidentified aircraft can be "picked up" when they call into a control center. The pilot will be asked to make a slight turn, and by an angled movement of the blip on the radar scanner the operator will know which of the blips represents the aircraft in question. A simpler method is involved with a device called a transponder. All commercial airline aircraft and many business family aircraft are equipped with this type of identification device which shows up on a radar unit. By pushing a button on the transponder unit the pilot sends out a signal which is picked up as a line on the control center scanner. It shows up right next to the blip which the airplane makes. Since a pilot flying cross country is following an airline road map, he can also plot his exact position and give that information to the control center.

RADIO NAVIGATION

One of the greatest aids to safe flying of the private plane has been the development of the VOR or omni radio navigation facilities. With the aid of the VOR facilities we now literally have "highways" in the sky. The country is dotted with hundreds of VOR (*V*ery High Frequency *O*mni-Directional *R*ange) radio stations. (Locations are shown on the charts.) These broadcast directional radio beams which radiate from each station like spokes from the hub of a wheel.

The aircraft omnirange receiver may be tuned in to any of the hundreds of VOR stations and a dial on the aircraft instrument panel may be set to tell the pilot what direction he should fly in order to proceed to the station or to fly along one of the "highways" which connect all of these stations. The dial will also tell if he inadvertently drifts off the "highway" and will even indicate which direction he should turn in order to get back onto it. Furthermore, by reading bearings from any two of these VOR stations, the pilot may plot a radio fix which will pinpoint his location on an aeronautical chart.

Almost every VOR station is linked to an FSS station, and fifteen minutes past the hour and fifteen before the hour, they interrupt the station's audible code signal to broadcast the latest weather. At any time they may also broadcast any special bulletins of interest to pilots en route and, of course, they supply all specific information the pilot may request. They also check on pilots who haven't reported at a check point at the time designated on flight plans.

Until the advent of VOR, the low-frequency radio range was the principal *air* navigational aid in the United States. Pilots making cross-country flights need not be proficient in complex orientation procedures on low frequency ranges. They will, however, find these ranges most helpful when used in connection with pilotage, dead reckoning, and omnirange flying, for directional guidance to determine position.

As electronic science progresses so will radio navigation. There are new products in the experimental stage and one or two have been placed on the market recently. One of these is the DME (distance measuring equipment). When a pilot tunes in a DME, his receiver indicator tells him in nautical miles how far he is from the station. In other words, new electronic products are taking the "work" out of air navigation (sometimes called *avigation*). Speaking of making things easy, automatic pilots (usually called *autopilots*) are now available to private plane owners. Such devices automatically control, to some extent, the flight of an airplane; usually it maintains the attitude of the plane and steers it on a course desired by the pilot. In an automobile, an autopilot would be equivalent to a device that would let you set the destination and relax for lunch, etc., while the driving is done for you.

NIGHT FLYING

While night flying is *not* required for your private license, some flight schools give at least one hour training. A few give up to five hours. Actually, the airplane is flown by night in the same way as it is by day, though more frequent reference should be made to the instruments to verify attitude, airspeed, heading, etc. A lesson or two in night flying will show up that there's nothing mysterious, dangerous, or particularly difficult about it.

There are, however, additional things to do at night

78

that are not necessary in day flight. For instance, you make the normal check before taxiing out, as by day, but in addition, you must check the night flying equipment such as landing lights, navigation lights, instrument and cabin lighting. The instrument lights should be adjusted to minimum intensity to allow for clearest view of external objects, to avoid undue tiring of the eyes, and to keep reflections off the windshield or windows to a minimum.

The principles of navigation are basically similar to those applicable by day, except that chart-reading at night calls for special technique. That is, it differs from that by day as landmarks, easily identifiable by day, can be so altered in appearance by the effect of darkness or of moonlight and shadow as to become quite indistinguishable. Ordinary chart-reading will generally be possible only under clear moonlight conditions when such features as lakes, rivers and coastlines show up particularly well. In addition, such visual aids as airport rotating beacons, etc., can be used, but it must be remembered that distances are difficult to judge when assessed by the position of stationary lights and that great accuracy is required when using such aids for calculating bearings and distances. Ground features will normally show up better when viewed against the moon. The airplane, of course, is navigated according to a predetermined flight plan which is corrected from time-to-time by use of the radio and visual aids available.

There are a few flight differences, too. For example, it's an important principle of night flying that you should be able to complete approaches and landings by reference to the runway lighting path only. The normal aid to judgment is the appearance of the runway lighting as seen after turning in on the final approach. If the approach path is correct, the flares or lights will appear to remain equidistant. If you're overshooting, the distance between the lights appears to increase; if undershooting, the distance appears to decrease. The aim, therefore, is to regulate the approach path so as to maintain the flare path in the correct perspective. As a matter of fact, the landing at night is made by visual reference to the flare path or runway lights. Owing to the deceptive appearance of the ground, no attempt should be made to refer to it as is done by day.

After a few dual sessions at night, you'll be able to go off on your own and be able to travel cross-country as easily as you do during the day.

THE WRITTEN TEST

During this time you will have been attending ground school or studying at home for the written test, a pre-requisite for the flight test. You'll be studying the following:

Navigation—Plotting courses, use of the compass, reading the navigation chart, computer work such as estimating flight time between points, estimating fuel consumption, and correcting for wind drift.

Radio—(Communications and radio navigation aids). You'll learn the communications and navigation services available to the pilot, including tower and Flight Service Station (ground communication station) functions and the use of the navigation aids.

Federal Aviation Regulations—The regulations for pilot certification and the "rules of the road" for flying are given here.

Aircraft Operations and Theory of Flight—The study of how the airplane flies, airplane loading and simple performance calculations. Tips on safety of operations are included.

As was just stated, you may either attend ground school or may study at home to prepare for this exam. Most ground schools use an audio-visual method of instruction such as the Sanderson course. All essential subjects are clearly presented in full-color photographs and drawings in conjunction with recordings which are keyed to textbooks and teaching aids. Since I attended ground school which used the audio-visual method, I may be partial in my thinking that this way of learning is superior However, if

80

time is a problem and you can't attend a ground school, the programmed type home-study course, such as the Jeppesen system, is very good. In this method, you read a short text, write your response and then check your answer. The programmed home course, which is a teacher machine type learning arrangement, is possibly the least expensive way of preparing for the written exam.

THE FLIGHT TEST

When your solo cross-country time requirement is completed and you have passed the written exam, you're ready for the flight test. The flight test is different from most examinations you've ever taken in that you'll know exactly what is required and will have discussed and practiced the procedures many times. The test is given either by an FAA inspector or a designated pilot examiner, and this check pilot will usually divide it into three basic parts:

1. *Oral Operational Examination*—You'll explain the papers required to be carried in the airplane and will show that you understand the airplane and power-plant logbooks and other inspection records. You will also discuss airplane performance and the effects of high temperatures on the take-off run (it will take a longer run than normal) and show that you have a good understanding of the cruising range of your airplane and the airspeeds for best performance. You'll also show that you can check the proper loading of the airplane and will make a thorough pre-flight inspection explaining, if asked, *why* you are checking a particular part of the airplane. By this time, you and the radio will be old friends, and you will demonstrate your proficiency in this regard.

2. *Basic Piloting Techniques*—You'll be judged on your starting, warmup and taxiing and will demonstrate the various types of take-offs and landings (cross-wind, short field, etc.) you've done so many times before. Stalls, slow flight and your ability to compensate for wind drift will be demonstrated to the check pilot. He will be inter-

ested during this phase on your general handling of the aircraft, with special emphasis on safety and judgment rather than absolute precision. You'll also show that you know the emergency operation of airplane equipment, as applicable.

3. *Cross-Country Flight*—Before taking off on the flight test, you'll be requested to plan a cross-country flight (checking weather, estimating flying time, fuel consumption, etc.). Usually, the check pilot will have you start out on the flight you planned and after he sees that you are able to follow the course and have a reasonable estimate of your ground-speed he will ask for a demonstration of your radio navigation skill and ability to fly by reference to the instruments (under the hood). He then may pick a nearby checkpoint or village and have you fly to it using the aeronautical chart as a reference. Part 3 is normally flown before Part 2, but the check pilot can vary the order if he likes.

If you are like many private applicants, you may contract a mysterious malady known as "checkitis" before the flight test. Usually the victim is of at least average intelligence but when checkitis strikes he is lucky to remember his own name. The malady is characterized by weak knees, a knotted stomach and loss of memory. If you get it, you'll be among thousands of *us* who have survived the attack. The good part about it is that after you get busy in the flight check its symptoms generally fade. Remember, you will have practiced all of the items of the flight test many times.

The flight test is your final hurdle. As a solo student, you haven't been able to carry passengers, but now you can take your family and friends into the wild blue yonder, and prove to them—as it had to be proved to you —that it isn't really wild.

Chapter 6

Fun and the Airplane

AFTER you have your license then the fun part of flying *really* begins. But, fun is many things to many pilots. Some find fun in the travel to other sports—to hunting and fishing, and a slope for skis. The airplane is a means to the end of what they consider a higher enjoyment. For others, the airplane is an end in itself; solving the problems of flight or perhaps guiding the path of a floatplane on the step serves as its own enjoyment. For most, however, the two are combined. A flight into history, for instance, is not an uncommon path for those who seek to know more of their country. They plan their flights to follow the still-visible wagon trails that cross the country from east to west, or to terminate in a town whose narrow and twisting streets once echoed to the tramp of redcoats' boots or the roar of Civil War cannons.

They define first what they enjoy, what they would like to see, and their airplane turns the plans into reality. They couldn't do it from an automobile; wagon ruts are not visible from the highway, and billboards that clutter the roads are not even noticeable without a determined search from the air. The airplane offers an invitation to a new way of life.

The best ideas for places to fly come from pilots who have been there. A portion of this chapter has been taken from a series of articles that appeared in *Flying Magazine*—written by pilots across the land who have flown their areas and know them well. They have suggested some starting points in travel and in an approach to fun.

NORTHEAST

A wobbly pile of slat-sided lobster traps in Maine vies with the dignified columnar edifice guarding the Plymouth Rock in Massachusetts to cast first shadow on the continent from the morning sun. The haze surrounding Manhattan's towers brightens. An instant later the Delaware Water Gap admits the first beams to eastern Pennsylvania, and the swirling vapors of Niagara begin to iridesce. The assembled collection of artifacts, history, metropolises and natural scenery in the northeastern states is among the most unlikely, but fascinating, anywhere.

Rubbing topographical shoulders together are picturesque lands that sheltered the first pilgrims, masonry flats bearing the nation's largest city, and some of the ruggedest unsullied outdoors country within the United States' borders. On the positive side, much of this area is more readily accessible by private airplane than by any other form of transportation. On the negative side, a glance at any weather map showing storm tracks will reveal that this is the most highly traversed section of the country. But the extra planning and foresight demanded are well worth the effort.

For those of sophisticated taste, the urban triad of New York City, Boston and Philadelphia offers unrivaled diversity in art, drama, theatre, museums—day and night life. For those more interested in *avoiding* the pace and strains of urban holidays, the northeast provides bountiful quantities of tranquil scenic hills, woodlands, lakes, rivers and mountains, in addition to the beach and marina-dotted seascape that meanders and weaves from New Jersey to Maine.

From the pilot's point of view, however, the essentials are not only that there be someplace to go or something to see, but that they be conveniently accessible by airplane.

84

For example, one of the most outstanding, especially for the landlocked, is a vast sandy stretch of seashore and resort hotels called Atlantic City. Best of all, an airport is located only four blocks from its broad surf-washed beaches and boardwalk. A well-fashioned set of runways called Bader Field unlocks the door to this remote stretch of Jersey beach, which sits well across barren pine forests from Camden and Philadelphia. The airport is just inland from the shore and the city's surprisingly built-up baroque palace hotel architecture. The trip from the airport to the beach can be made by bus, on the roadway adjacent to the field. At best it represents no more than a short salt-air walk right to the seaside.

But if you're surfeited with the smell of salt water and candied apples, and willing to make an interesting swap, head your airplane west and north toward Pennsylvania, past Philadelphia in the direction of the capital at Harrisburg. En route, before you have crossed the Delaware River, you will approach a unique example of aviation enterprise called the Flying "W" airport. For a combination of horseback hospitality, airplane-shaped swimming pool and restaurant, all tailored to the whims of the vacationing pilot, this is well worth a visit. The airfield is just east of Moorestown, New Jersey.

When you have resumed your flight northwest again, you can cruise over the Lancaster "Pennsylvania Dutch" region and observe the even, lush farmlands of the quaint Amish people. They represent a little portion of history from an earlier era, and if you hold a low altitude, you might even spot the horses and buggies they use exclusively for transportation, and catch the bright glints of color called "Hex signs" used to decorate the barns.

Just short of the Susquehanna River you will find a hillside emblazoned in white letters: "Welcome to Hershey." Right off the base of the hill is a trim little grass meadow. The adjoining T-hangars and landing lights identify it as the Hershey Air Park. If the wind is blowing in the right way, your nose will give positive second identification that you have reached the home of the "chocolate town." Actually this little hamlet is one of the most attractive places to visit in the east because of its diversity of activities for the visitor.

But if you've time for more holiday sightseeing in Pennsylvania, one of the most interesting historical areas in the nation lies just to the southwest across the Susquehanna. Head out over the capitol buildings at Harrisburg and down to the site of the most famous of Civil War battles: Gettysburg. Two airports, Gettysburg and Doersom, serve this area.

For a change of pace, head your airplane back to Harrisburg and follow the undulations of the scenic Susquehanna due north right to the bend at Williamsport. Beyond Williamsport over rugged Pennsylvania hill country lies Elmira, New York and some of the most delightful spectator (or participant) sport for any pilot. Located here is the scenic Harris Hill Gliderport, with a sailplane launch right out over the valley.

Beckoning just over the horizon to the northwest is Niagara Falls, well worth a special trip and an overflight, if you're in the area. Both Buffalo and Niagara Falls airports serve this area, where the Niagara River joins Lakes Erie and Ontario in spectacular fashion.

Our next destination will be just on the other side of Burlington, Vermont, over the broad waters of Lake Champlain. And this will be New England's most famous ski land, the Stowe-Mount Mansfield ski area. Skiers from all over New England and as far south as New York City and beyond travel the almost day-long car trip for a chance at these outstanding ski slopes. Weather permitting, the pilot has the advantage here, as a 2,850-foot airfield, the Morrisville State Airport, is located just six miles north of Stowe. The field is kept plowed during the winter months, and the ski area is accessible by taxi. By the way, all too many pilots think along the lines of boatmen; the moment snow appears they put their airplane away and flee the premises in horror, leaving their little beauties shunned and scorned in the back of the hangar until spring sets in. A fie on such notions. Winter flying is fun, too.

If it's rugged outdoor life, hunting or fishing you're after, set your directional gyro for Maine. This state has some of the most wide-open, unsullied countryside in the northeast. But if it's boat quays, fishing villages and salt spray you're after, head southeast to such places as Bar Harbor or Rockland (both with hard-surfaced airports). Maine, of course, is the home of a vast lobster industry, and you can assuage a hankering for this seafood dish almost anywhere. If you're in Rockland the first weekend in August, a three-day seafood festival featuring lobster served outdoors, parades, etc. should satisfy your crustacean cravings.

One of the most popular vacationlands of the New England area, however, comprises Cape Cod to the south of Boston, and the adjoining islands. Martha's Vineyard offers airports that admit the pilot traveler and family to a tranquil little island bordered with pleasant beaches and colored chalk cliffs. You won't find a billboard on the island. But watch out for the weather. A local phenomenon is a quick moving cloud bank that will shroud the island without warning while the rest of New England remains sunny and clear.

Nantucket Island nearby is renowned for its antique colonial setting, cobblestone streets and beautiful old homes and buildings—and as a honeymooners' haunt. But for a pleasant setting recalling the old New England whaling and fishing days, there is a unique little community not far to the west along the Connecticut coast. This is the Mystic Seaport and Marine Museum at Mystic. Here an entire seaport and village has been restored with old sailing ships and various artifacts. Although not immediately adjacent, the Trumbull Airport at nearby Groton is close enough to serve this picturesque anachronism with its big three-masted windjammers tied up along the docks.

Traveling on down the Connecticut coast to the west you will fly over one of the country's unique summer

Airplanes on floats are used extensively in coastal areas and in inland lake country. Most of these are used for business and charter purposes.

theatres, well worth an afternoon or evening visit if Shakespeare is your dish of tea. Land at the Bridgeport Airport, and a short cab ride to nearby Stratford brings you to the American Shakespeare Festival Theatre. This non-profit foundation presents two or more of the Bard's plays during each summer season at an intriguing polygonal theatre patterned after the original Shakespearean theatre at Stratford-on-Avon in England. Top notch, well-known actors often participate in these plays.

From Bridgeport, it's only a short hop across Long Island Sound to the fabulous "Long Island." Here there are several small airports, plus Kennedy and La Guardia—the key airfields to New York City. Other airports serving the "big city" include Teterboro, Westchester, and Newark.

SOUTHEAST

Each region in this big magnificent land has its own distinctive appeals and characteristic charms; the mountains, the plains and the ocean shores. But there is perhaps no single area that combines such a wide choice of year-round travel attractions as you can find within the narrow boundaries of the southeast. Here you have hills, lofty mountains, numerous lakes and endless beaches. What makes the area outstanding is that it extends deep into the tropical sea. Here are facilities for sport and recreation, and resorts to suit all tastes and desires, all within reach of an airport, and many even have their own landing fields.

Historically it ranks as one of the most distinguished areas of the land. From the days of discovery it still bears the footprints of the conquerors, the tracks of explorers and pioneers, the remains of old homesteads and plantations of early settlers, and the hallowed grounds of battle on which the republic was founded. St. Augustine boasts of the oldest settlement and fortification; it is also the site where Ponce De Leon reputedly found the Fountain of Youth. The trail of De Soto's exploits ranges far north into the Carolina mountains. In Virginia there is James-

town, the site of the first permanent English colony; York-
town, where Washington triumphed; and Williamsburg,
which is now fully restored. Fort Sumter lies on an island
in Charleston Harbor, and Kitty Hawk, the memorial of
man's first powered flight, rises from the sand dunes off the
Carolina coast.

The southeastern area starts at Washington, D. C. and
is conveniently close to the big cities of the north. Most
points in the area can be reached in a day in a moderately
fast airplane. There are three distinct flyways, each different and marked by its own inherent features and attractions. At Washington they part and spread widely between
the mountains and the sea. They join in the southernmost
state and terminate in the Florida Keys in a narrow single
lane. If poring over the map in spring, autumn or summer,
a choice would be hard to make because of the diversity of
appeals. However, in winter one probably would pick the
central skyway in pursuit of the Florida sun.

The least traveled route probably is the one skirting
the Atlantic shore. Much of it runs over and near open
water and it has more than its share of weather pitfalls. But
it also has its rewards in its remote unruffled beaches, good
fishing resorts, excellent seafood and its picturesque gardens and plantation estates.

If you're looking at the map in spring, summer or 'fall,
bent on a holiday cruise offering exciting views, a refreshing brisk climate and vigorous outdoor sports, a good
choice would be the western skyway that follows the Ap-
palachian Mountains through Virginia and the Carolinas
into Georgia. For scenic grandeur it's the most spectacular route. In spring and in autumn the scenery is most bril-
liant and festive. In spring a huge carpet of pink and white
fruit tree blossoms covers the floor and sides of Shenan-
doah Valley. In early summer patches of wildflowers, rho-
dodendron and mountain laurel light up the dark green
slopes of the Smoky Mountains, and in the late season
the Blue Ridge and the Smokies erupt in a blaze of autumn
colors. On the way south from here, the mountains drop

off quickly and yield to the rolling hills of Georgia. The terrain gradually levels off as it approaches the Florida border and merges with the central flyway.

If you're heading south to catch the Florida sun, try the central flyway. Like U. S. Highway No. 1, it follows the easy route through the lowlands of Virginia and the Carolinas and joins the other skyways near the Georgia-Florida border. It's the quickest and most direct route from the north and it is the least hampered by weather. From Washington south it follows the Potomac to Fredericksburg where it continues overland to Richmond, Virginia, and Raleigh, North Carolina, and down to the coast to Savannah, Brunswick, Georgia, and to Jacksonville, Florida. This route contacts the big southern cities, all of which have good city airports. For alternate stops, Rocky Mount, Lumberton, Sumter and Orangeburg provide good landing facilities with nearby accommodations. For more extended stays in the lowlands, there are resort areas at Southern Pines in North Carolina, near Camden and Aiken in South Carolina, and on the islands off Brunswick, Georgia. St. Simons Island and Jekyll Island have airports.

Landing facilities for the touring flier are plentiful throughout Florida. Most major resort centers provide several airports. The choice should depend on convenience. There are airports and flight strips at many out-of-the-way places and at some of the sight-seeing attractions. Landing fields can be found at Silver Springs and at Cypress Gardens, at the town of Everglades in Everglades National Park, and on Sanibel Island. To the flier who is reluctant to venture out over the water, it should be reassuring to know that there are now seven airports, quite evenly spaced, among the Florida Keys.

NORTH CENTRAL

Whether your airplane is two-, four-, or six-place—whether it can cruise at 110, 145, or 250 mph—it can be the key to virtually unlimited adventure, fun and frolic in

Golfers often get up flying foursomes and travel to play many interesting or unusual courses which are within easy range by air.

the North Central area of the United States. In this region, 11 states combine to offer almost any type of natural or man-made attraction to appeal to a carefree or serious mood of a pilot on holiday or just out for a weekend.

The terrain in this part of the country is of the easy-to-fly type. But it's interesting with large areas of flat, fertile lands, rolling hills, and occasionally along the edge of the region a relatively short chain of razor-back hills which can be flown safely, when cruising at a level between 5,000 to 7,000 feet. In most of the airspace over the 11 states is an invisible, giant matrix of overlapping omni radials and low-frequency ranges along with non-directional radio beacons. Navigation by use of radio aids is a pleasure. Weather data is readily available via radio. Likewise, navigation by pilotage is interesting and uncomplicated. There are numerous lakes, rivers, cities, highways, railroads, and section lines upon which to orient—or follow, for that matter. The area is liberally sprinkled with airports of all sizes. No flight need be more than two or three hours between fuel or comfort stops if you wish.

Where to go and what to see is really a matter of first determining your interest, as of the moment. Once this is established, then it is easy to plot a course to one of the many places within range of the family-type airplane, such as:

For informal and relaxed living with a strong nautical overlay, there are the Erie Islands. This group of islands in the western end of Lake Erie—just north of the Sandusky, Ohio omni—offers a vacation land only one hour's flight from Cleveland, Toledo, or Detroit. Here one can find wonderful swimming beaches, good fishing, excellent waters for sail and power boating, and a pace of life free from the pressures of business and commerce.

For the flair of cosmopolitan life and city wonders, you will gravitate toward the cities with "close in" airports. It's very convenient to land at the lake front airports of Chicago or Cleveland, and be in the heart of the activity within minutes after landing. Memphis, too, offers a

93

"downtown strip" along the river, just minutes away from adventures in good eating or interesting shops. And then there is Detroit City Airport situated deep near the heart of the automobile capital of the world. Likewise, Holman Field at St. Paul, Minnesota, offers multirunway facilities, practically at the foot of its downtown section.

For early American atmosphere, visit historic and colorful Mackinac Island located in northern Michigan. First explored by Jean Nicolet in 1634, the island reflects vividly the atmosphere of the early French, the British, the 1796 American, and the rough and tumble fur trapper who sold his skins to John Jacob Astor's American Fur Company. Since no vehicles are allowed on the island, you must land your flying machine at St. Ignace on the mainland. The airport offers friendly service; the hard-surfaced runway is 3,200 feet long and lines up with the prevailing wind. Elevation of the airport is 600 feet with clear approaches. The ride by car into town takes but 10 or 15 minutes. The ferry ride (delightful and very pleasant) to Mackinac Island from St. Ignace is about 40 minutes.

For an adventure in the history of flight, point the nose of your airplane to the "Birthplace of Aviation." This is Dayton, Ohio, home of the Wright brothers. Just 11 miles from this city is located Wright-Patterson Air Force Base, which houses the Air Force Museum. To visit the museum, the best spot to land is at Dayton's Municipal Airport, and then rent a car.

For a flight backward in time into the "Days of '76"— complete with gold mines, Indians, buffalo and hard-riding cowboys—hold a heading to the Black Hills of South Dakota. Here, in the once sacred land of the proud Sioux, you can explore this region of forest-draped hills and grassy valleys, and live close to the historic past of our Wild West. You can land at Rapid City, the eastern gateway to the "hills."

For king-size sporting events, try the Kentucky Derby, run at Churchill Downs in Louisville since 1875, and the Indianapolis Memorial Day 500-mile automobile race

Both places are served by a number of good airports. One choice is Bowman Field when going to the Derby, and Sky Harbor Airport when taking in the auto classic.

For escape into a woodland wonderland dotted with 10,000 lakes of sparkling waters, answer the call of northern Minnesota. Here you will find good fishing and deer hunting; scattered around the state are large numbers of prehistoric Indian mounds; you can view the largest open pit iron mine in the world; you can enjoy some 31 state parks noted for their scenic beauty and interesting features. Some 140 airports and landing fields are scattered about the state; however, in the northern portion many are unattended. If the field is unattended, make a low pass over the strip and give it a good visual check before landing.

SOUTH CENTRAL

Cruising down the Mississippi River may well be the theme of one of the most enjoyable flying vacations you can make in the South Central states. If you have never flown along at low (but safe) altitude, following the course or shoreline of a river observing the many natural and historic interests, you have missed many a piloting pleasure. And, in this region, there's never a lack of places to explore for rivers and coastline cover the land. The Mississippi and its tributaries alone extend from within 250 miles of the Atlantic Ocean to a point just 500 miles from the Pacific. You can throw a stick in a small creek in upstate New York and have it turn up a few weeks later in New Orleans. And the river extends from Canada to the Gulf; there are over 15,000 miles of inland waterways in this system. Regardless of where you are or your river's name, it is fun to explore, interesting to follow.

Your flight down the Mississippi River Valley might be just a 10-mile stretch along the Cimarron or a 50-mile jaunt down the Red to where it enters Lake Texoma between Texas and Oklahoma. It may be down the full 980 miles of the even-width Ohio from where the Monongahela and the Allegheny rivers join to where it enters the Missis-

sippi at Càiro, Illinois. Perhaps you may like flying somewhere along the 2,500-mile-long Missouri River, but the
trip we like to make is down the Mississippi to the Gulf
and then around the coast to Corpus Christi.

Starting our trip at Hannibal, Missouri, on the right
bank we'll fly over the home of Samuel Clemens (Mark
Twain) famous for his Huck Finn and Tom Sawyer
stories. He was born about five miles away in the small
town of Florida but Hannibal claims the fame. The Illinois
River enters from Chicago and Lake Michigan. Then
Alton, Illinois—its little known that Alton is the spot
where died the famous New Orleans privateer, Jean Laf-
fite. Then from the west, the great Missouri River enters.
At this point it is actually larger than the Mississippi for it
has run its full 2,500 miles while the Mississippi has come
a mere 1,700.

St. Louis is the birthplace of the *St. Louis Blues* and the
first thought of Lindbergh's Spirit of St. Louis. This is the
largest city on the Mississippi, about twice the size of New
Orleans, and was the historic stepping-off place for the
early West. Today it is a cultural center of the Midwest.
There are at least a dozen airports in the vicinity of St.
Louis.

The river continues south and eastward after leaving
St. Louis, Crystal City, St. Genevieve and the orphan town
of Kaskaskia, Illinois—on the west shore, put there by a
change in channel of the fickle stream. Perryville has an
airport near the river. Then south again, by Cape Girar-
deau, a paved airport here and then a double horseshoe
bend in the river before the Ohio is allowed to enter at
Cairo, Illinois.

The shores are now marked by many lakes and canals
which have been formed by overflows of the river. The
general course is now southward and soon a large city
looms on the eastern shore. We have been flying over cotton country for some time but here is the Cotton King,
Memphis, Tennessee. It lies on a bluff overlooking the
river and has always been looked on as the stevedore

town; Memphis is noted for its river traffic. You might want to divert at this point for a visit to the health spa of the South, Hot Springs, Arkansas, which lies 175 miles to the west.

After leaving Memphis, the state of Mississippi is now on the left bank, lakes and bayous increase in number in the vicinity of the main stream, and levees appear on both shores. The St. Francis River flows in from the west just above Helena, Arkansas, and a paved airport is just 10 miles northwest of the city. About 50 miles south, the White and Arkansas Rivers, having come all the way from beyond Wichita, Kansas, enter.

Lake Providence is next with its lake-bordered airport and then Vicksburg. Here was fought the battle which broke the Confederate back. Grant would have given much for the view of Vicksburg that is afforded from a private airplane. The Vicksburg National Military Park and Cemetery is worth a visit.

Natchez, oldest city on the Mississippi, rises next. Dating back to 1716 when founded as Fort Rosalie by Bienville, Natchez was one of the wealthiest cities in this country prior to the Civil War. Many of the ante-bellum homes are maintained in immaculate condition and each year during March there is a pilgrimage when the homes are opened to the public. South of Natchez, you will largely be over marshland. For about 25 miles the Oachita River parallels the Mississippi before becoming the Black River and joining the Red. Part of this stream enters the Mississippi while some of it continues south in the form of the Atchafalaya River which flows independently to the Gulf. If you fly in from the west, the Atchafalaya is easy to mistake for the Mississippi.

Baton Rouge, the next major landmark and Louisiana's capitol, is the northernmost deep water port on the Mississippi and you have a choice of Ryan Field on the north side of town and the Downtown Airport on the southeast side. There are a dozen horseshoe bends between Baton Rouge and New Orleans and river activity is noticeably increased. Barges and ocean liners pass in the stream. You pass Moisant Airport before reaching New Orleans, but it might be to your advantage to land at the New Orleans Lake Front Airport on Lake Pontchartrain.

New Orleans is approximately 110 miles from the end of the delta. Upon leaving the delta you may follow the coastline to Grand Isle, then follow the road across the marshland to Houma, then across to Patterson. There are airports at both towns. Then cut across to the north side of Marsh Island and back again to the coast. Now you're in a good position to follow the coastline all the rest of the way. You might have decided to visit Lafayette where the largest heliport in the world is located or continue down the mud coast of Louisiana toward Texas.

Ahead, we find the mud banks turning to sand as we approach Texas. Offshore are the inevitable oil rigs. This is work and play country. Ahead is the San Jacinto Monument and the battleship Texas. Houston, Galveston, on down the coast to Corpus Christi, we can go inland to the valley or cross-country to San Antonio and its Alamo, or westward to Fort Clark, the reconstructed cavalry post that now serves as a guest ranch at Brackettville, Texas. Or perhaps to the Dallas-Forth Worth area to visit Six Flags over Texas, the Disneyland of the Southwest. Or to Oklahoma City and down the Canadian River—but that is another story.

NORTHWEST

The northwest is a pilot's paradise because it has everything—lakes, streams, deserts, and rain forests, petrified forests, boating, swimming, fishing, skiing, mountain-climbing, spelunking, timber carnivals, barbecues, rodeos, dude ranches, air resorts, ghost towns, goat-watching, primitive areas and sophisticated "niteries"—all easily air-accessible. It has 90 per cent of the glaciers and most of the mountains of the original 48 states. These ranges demand respect. But don't let them scare you away. The covered wagons crossed them and so can you.

There are three natural gateways—north, south and central. The front door route is the route of the covered wagons. You can still see their tracks rutted deep in a few spots if you know where to look. Actually, the best route usually depends upon the weather. You can check that at Colorado Springs, where the West begins, and check out the Broadmoor, one of the country's oldest, biggest and most sophisticated spas, while you're at it. Take your choice of golf, tennis, swimming, riding, nightclubbing or ice skating year round. Don't miss the Garden of the Gods and the Air Force Academy 10 miles north as you take off. This aerial ogling is half the fun of flying.

Land at Aspen's Pitkin County field, adequate for single-engine aircraft and light twins, and just three miles from one of the country's most famous ski slopes, also a summer fun spot. Gunnison also has an airline airport, 35 miles from the new Crested Butte ski area. Steamboat Springs, another noted ski and summer sports area, has a 3,400-foot runway at 6,920 feet.

Wyoming is a wasteland, but with a number of aerial oases, like Jackson Hole on the Snake River, near Jackson Lake, gateway to the Grand Teton National Park. Jackson Hole is also a gateway to Yellowstone Park with its 3,000 geysers, hot springs, lakes and natural wonders. West Yellowstone has the best airport, however, used by airliners and open the year round (although the park is not). Yellowstone Park itself is quite impressive from the air. So is the Devil's Tower, on the Belle Fourche River south of Hulett, and Teapot Rock south of Midwest on Highway 87. Thermopolis, which claims the world's biggest hot springs, boasts a 4,535-foot runway.

In summer, many pilots like the northern route across Montana, The Land of the Big Sky, wide open country where a single water tank or ranch spread is a major checkpoint. The next west is Idaho, the flyingest state in the union outside of Alaska. North of Boise lies the last of the forest primeval on the original "mainland" United States, three million acres of wilderness. Here is a land the Lord locked away in a vault made of mountains—and threw away the key. Only the airplane can unlock the door to this land of the murmuring pine and the larch. Access by highway is forbidden. No mining, logging or grazing is allowed. You come laboriously on foot or horseback—unless you have wings. There are about 30 listed fields here, out of Idaho's 200 airfields. But some can be marginal at times.

If you're the cautious type you can land at Orofino Municipal, or Floating Feather airport near Boise to get the latest information on the wilderness strips, or get a mountain man to fly you in. Typical of a half-dozen air resorts in the back of beyond is Sulphur Creek Ranch, at the 5,550-foot elevation, 3,000 feet long, two miles from Morgan's Ranch on the La Grande sectional. Land upstream and roll to a stop in front of a rustic cabin bordering the strip. You may have to argue the right-of-way with a band of deer or elk. Moose Creek Ranch near Orofino, Flying B Ranch 25 miles out of Challis and a few others in the primitive area offers meals and guest ranch accommodations. None are plush country clubs, since everything including the kitchen sink and the electric generator has to be flown in.

Idaho is one of the first states in the country to offer free picnic parks and campgrounds for pilots only. Typical is Johnson Creek Airstrip, 3,553 feet of sod at 4,900 feet elevation. It's complete with tie-downs, picnic tables, camp stoves, drinking water, garbage disposal and firewood, just like a highway park—but without the highway. A shelter with bunks is provided for fliers who bring their own sleeping bags. Similar campgrounds are provided at Cascade Reservoir Air Strip on the banks of Cascade Reservoir and at Cavanaugh Bay Airport on Priest Lake, near a fishing resort; also at Big Creek and Warm Springs Creek on the South Fork of the Payette River—all on good fishing grounds.

At the end of the Old Oregon Trail lies the Beaver State, almost as airminded as Idaho, with 30 state-built fields opening up the far corners to the adventuring pilot. On Pelican Point in the Owhyee Reservoir in the desert country of eastern Oregon you can land and fish off the end of the runway for bass, crappie and perch, best fishing of its kind in the state. It's for pilots only, can't be reached by road. Don't miss Crater Lake, on the crest of the Cascades, 55 miles northwest of Klamath Falls. The sapphire blue of this lake, deepest in the United States (1,996 feet), six miles in diameter, can only be appreciated from the air.

Biggest, most luxurious resort on the Pacific's sands is Ocean Shores, a $50 million new resort city on the 330-degree radial of Grays Harbor VOR. From the 2,700-foot surfaced runway you can walk a block to motels, night clubs, cabins and the beach. Look out for golf balls on approach. You're landing in a golf course, surrounded by lake and surf fishing, deep sea fishing, clamming and social life that attracts visitors and investors from faraway places.

The San Juan Islands of Puget Sound are among the nation's most charming and most air-accessible. Answer to a pilot's dream is Blakely Island, 75 miles southeast of Bellingham, Washington, private Bali Hai of 150 pilot-owners, who came from as far as 1,000 miles away to spend their summers and weekends here. This is an aviation estate, with only a few home sites still for sale—to pilots only. But visitors are welcome to drop in, feed the score of wild deer, so tame they will climb into your airplane if you tempt them; hike through the quiet woods; swim in the bay or lakes; fish; or dine, drink and hangar-fly at Blakely House, the island club-house and restaurant. The motel, with only a dozen apartments at the most modest prices, is usually filled, but reservations can be made in advance.

Like to try goat-watching? Land at Stehekin River Airport at the head of Lake Chelan, deep in the heart of the Cascades, 2,700 feet long, 1,488-foot elevation. Mountain goats come down to the lake to drink at evening. Or you

Many resorts, such as Rancho de los Caballeros, on the desert near Wickenburg, Arizona, cater to the fly-in trade by having private landing strips right on their grounds.

can stay at Stehekin Lodge and stalk them in their high mountain lairs.

Seattle, Washington's king city, is its biggest single tourist attraction next to Mount Rainier National Park itself. Most convenient "side entrance" to Seattle is Bellevue's 2,250-foot runway, 10 miles northeast of downtown Seattle by handy bus or helicopter. It boasts lights, a small cafe, and just across the highway, Pantley's Pagan Hut, a famous motel and night club with top shows nightly.

Lake Tahoe, straddling the Nevada-California line, famous for swimming, boating and summer resorts as well as gambling casinos, has its own Lake Tahoe airport at the south end of the lake, plus Truckee-Tahoe, northwest of the lake, which is the aerial gateway to Squaw Valley, famous Olympic ski area and summer resort as well.

SOUTHWEST

The attractions of the Southwest are such that literally, there's something for everybody. To recite a few of the better known—Los Angeles, with its suburbs of Hollywood, Beverly Hills, Malibu and, on a fairly clear night, probably the largest unbroken carpet of lights anywhere in the world. There is skiing in the mountains en route to Los Angeles, in the high mountain country of New Mexico. Hoover Dam, Lake Mead and, of course, Las Vegas, are added attractions. If you like ghost towns, or towns with the old mining flavor, try Tonopah, Nevada, or Rhyolite, California, or Virginia City, Nevada, or, well that list goes on and on.

If you want to come during the winter and share the golf course, there's Palm Springs. Or there's Phoenix, Wickenburg or Tucson, Arizona, if you want less expensive sunny winter climate.

To second guess airborne vacationers just a bit, it would seem that Indians, authentic in all respects, would be one of the biggest attractions of the Southwest. In street clothes, "you can't tell 'em without a program." But they do honor their traditions at several sites and times during vacation season. Starting with New Mexico, one of the biggest Indian affairs is held in Gallup, beginning the second Thursday of August of each year, with some 30 tribes or groups participating. Photography rules are liberal (not all Indian ceremonials can be photographed, you know). Best thing to do is write ahead in ample time to get accommodations. There is an admission charge, and more data can be had from the Inter-Tribal Indian Ceremonial Association, Gallup, New Mexico.

In Arizona, the annual All-Indian Pow-Wow is held at Flagstaff for three days during the July 4 weekend. During the last 10 days in August the famous Hopi Indian snake dances are held in the Hopi villages in the northeast part of the state. Entrance is from airports at Holbrook, Winslow or Tuba City. Also in early August, the businessmen and wives in Prescott, Arizona, stage the Smoki Ceremonials, in which they, the white people, perpetuate the authentic Indian dances. Again, if planning to attend any of the events, by all means write ahead for confirmed reservations. People come from all over the world for these ceremonials, and it's first come, first served. Other good stops in New Mexico are Taos and Santa Fe.

Passing along to Arizona, the first thing which comes to mind is the Grand Canyon. Here, especially beautiful to the airman and his family are sunrise and sunset, either viewed from the rim of the canyon on the ground, or from the air. This is one of the world's great wonders of nature, not easily described verbally. But it alone is worth a trip West—ask anyone who's seen it.

Again, for the special-interest people, at the end of the Grand Canyon, so to speak, is Lake Mead and water sports, fishing—you name it. En route down the canyon one passes the Kaibab, one of the most noted deer hunting spots in the nation.

If you're a little north of Grand Canyon, on the Utah side, there is Monument Valley, shared by both Utah and

Arizona which is dotted by airports, as is New Mexico, Utah and parts of Nevada. However, many of these are in the mountains. The Arizona state aeronautical chart has excellent mountain flying tips on the back. This valuable information applies to Utah, Idaho, New Mexico, Colorado, Wyoming, Montana, California, Mexico and all.

From Nevada or Arizona, the next step is Southern California. Being a native, there are many things we take for granted which are musts for visitors. The Los Angeles area needs no talking about. It has smog, millions of cars, Hollywood, and freeways. But there are extras, such as the Mt. Palomar 200-inch telescope, and there's an excellent landing field at Palomar, the town, nearby.

North of Los Angeles there is Yosemite National Park, with the famed falls and scenery. On the eastern slopes of the Sierra Madre mountains are the Big Lakes, with airports and facilities for fishermen.

If you hanker for salt water, Southern California can give it to you either inland or on the ocean. The Salton Sea, lowest spot in the North American Continent (at one town on its edge), is a booming resort-retirement site. Water sports are here, no fishing. On the Southern California shore there is Santa Catalina Island, a resort with a landing field easily reached from Los Angeles basin area. The channel is only 24 miles across; you can still see the Los Angeles area while in the Catalina pattern.

The Southwest is very airplane-conscious. There are more airplanes in this area than any comparable one in the nation. The airports are good. A very large percentage are paved. Usually there are accommodations nearby which are reasonable in price. There are exceptions, of course; there always are.

OTHER PLACES TO FLY

As we said earlier, an airplane is a unique vehicle, capable of travel over land or water. While our description of places to fly has been confined to the original 48 states, Alaska, our 49th, is one of the flyingest states in the union. Airports and landing strips are plentiful and scenery is beyond mere words.

It will most likely be quite a number of years before the business family plane pilot can take off from the United States mainland and fly the 2,636-odd miles to our 50th State. There's just too much ocean and no stopping-off places in between. Nevertheless, private flying in Hawaii, though small at present, is on the increase. And for the resident of the state who has a flying license, the opportunities of visiting the islands to the upmost are ideal.

Canada is an excellent first-time-out-of-the-country trip for newer pilots. The "paper work" crossing the border between the United States and Canada is very simple since there are no inoculations required, plus there's no money exchange or language difficulties. Airports and landing areas are very plentiful, and lodging and eating spots are easy to find. Unlike the United States National Parks, Canada's two most famous ones—Banff and Jasper—have landing fields *within* the Parks' borders. Actually, the whole country of Canada is a pilot's dream. Fishing and hunting is unlimited to the sportsman-flier.

Mexico, the Islands of the Caribbean, and the Bahamas are other ideal flight trips. In the case of the latter, whether you just visit Nassau and one or two of the lesser known islands, or pull all the stops and follow the trail of the Treasure Hunters, you've got a treat in store. For nowhere in this Hemisphere is the water clearer or more colorful, the fishing better or more varied, the breezes balmier or the natives more friendly. And nowhere in the world will the private flier find a more agreeable "welcome" mat—this one woven in native straw with a hat to match. Every trip to the Bahamas by private plane involves customs papers and proper clearance, but the airfield operators at West Palm, Fort Lauderdale, or Miami will help to make things easy for the uninitiated.

TAKE YOUR CAMERA UPSTAIRS

On any trip—whether by car, bus, train or plane—you'll want to have your camera along to record it. But in an airplane, you can take photos of the places you and your family visit that could *not* be taken on the land. Are special cameras required for aerial photography? Not at all. Any hand-held model will do the trick, from the simplest to the most complex. Of course, the more versatile cameras can take pictures of a greater range of aerial subjects. For instance, if your interest is in a record shot of the ground from a reasonably high altitude, a box camera will do nicely. If you have a more expensive camera with a faster lens and shutter, you will be able to take a great number of action pictures from the air, as well. Let's say that you have a good, fast, 35-mm camera with wide angle and telephoto lenses. With a combination like this you can cover the whole range of aerial photography.

As to shutter speeds, these will depend on your altitude, but because of the inherent vibration of the plane, a camera with at least 1/250 is most desirable. The plane's vibration, primarily caused by the engine, will distort the photos if the shutter speed is too slow. Be sure there aren't any cloud shadows on the ground and pick a clear sunny day for best results. An exposure meter is recommended, of course, and use the fastest film you can get.

Fortunately focus isn't a problem. Since aerial photos are rarely taken at altitudes less than 300 feet above the ground, the lens can be set at infinity and left there for the duration of the flight.

With the obliques you'll get your real fun in flying photography. Here is where you can compete with the long-haired boys on the ground for composition, dramatic effects or straight pictorials. Oblique pictures are those resulting when you point your camera at an angle to the ground. Normally these are taken at about a 30-degree angle. As in a ground portrait, the light should be shining on the front of your subject. If the light is coming from a

45-degree angle over your right shoulder as you take the picture, you will also have the help of the shadow angle in making your ground objects stand out better with a three-dimensional effect.

The closer you get to your subject, the faster you'll have to act. Sometimes you have only a two-second period in which to take the picture before the speed of the airplane has taken you out of range. On a large subject area, which means that you will be shooting farther away, you may get 5 to 7 seconds or longer in which to frame the subject and snap the shutter. In any case you will have to be on your toes. It's particularly true with a small camera that your subject should fill the negative area. This, of course, means you'll have to move in close, and the closer you come the faster the shutter speed must be to stop the action and get a sharp, clear negative. Even for a picture on the ground, it's best to use at least 1/100 exposure to insure against camera movement. In the air 1/200 is the least for a distant shot. Within 1,000 feet, it's best to use at least 1/400, or even higher speeds if your camera has a focal plane shutter. If your camera does not have these speeds you will just have to take your pictures from a greater distance.

The subject of filters must come up in any discussion of pictorial photography. Usually you can get along without them, because most of your shooting is done only in the better, sunny days. In aerial photography, however, filters serve an additional purpose that usually does not have to be considered on the ground. They cut through aerial haze. There is always moisture in the air, and this acts as a multitude of tiny prisms, breaking up the light to give the effect of haze. A deep yellow or red filter will cut right through it to give you more detail in the distance. This haze is predominantly blue in color and unfortunately most film emulsions are abnormally sensitive to blue. Therefore, it's not a bad idea to make use of a medium-yellow filter at all times. Remember, a medium-yellow filter will help you get darker skies so that clouds will stand out well. It will also cut haze a little. Orange or light red will definitely cut aerial haze and give you abnormally dramatic, dark sky and cloud effects.

Color aerial photography is just as practical as the ground variety. Slower shutter speeds have to be used, or faster lenses because the film is slower. It requires a little more care, but good results are well worth while.

Here are a few hints which will help you take bigger and better aerial pictures. Before taking off to shoot a subject, be sure that the light is going to be in the most favorable position. Look at your map and figure out the course you must fly in order to bring you "on target." You'll save a lot of valuable flying time that way.

For dramatic effects, keep an eye out for sweeping designs and contrasting patterns in the variegated tapestry of the ground. To increase contrast and create a feeling of depth in the picture, establish points of reference by framing the scene in a window or windshield, or by including part of the wing, the nose of the plane or an engine nacelle.

You now have an outline of the basic principles and equipment required for aerial photography. The only item lacking is practice.

FAMILY FLYING FUN CHECKLIST

You'll want to take off at every opportunity for interesting and varied destinations. There's no need to schedule every trip at the height of the tourist season. You can take more trips to more places by plane, and the school holidays (teachers' convention, Thanksgiving, semester break) afford the perfect opportunities. You'll discover that "off season" rates can be surprisingly low.

By flying you can stay long enough to really enjoy yourself. For instance, during the ski season, Skitch Henderson, who wrote the foreword for this book, does a great deal of of flying. "When I fly, I rent airplanes, usually from Teterboro Air Service at Teterboro Airport. Most of my flying

Family travel fun is available through the use of personal aircraft. Many flying families share aircraft costs with "joint ownership" plan or by joining one of the hundreds of flying clubs in the U.S. and abroad.

is spent in commuting between New York City and Sugarbush, Vermont, where my family lives in the winter," Skitch explains. "It's just 65 minutes by plane, while it takes almost 9 hours by car."

"Frequently I fly alone. I find that flying cleanses both my mind and my soul. Many of the most successful arrangements have been developed—in the formative state —while I was behind the controls of a light plane on a cross-country trip. There is that essential time for meditation that is one of the best ways to produce really good music.

"One of the best things about flying your own plane: no rigid schedules. On Sunday afternoons, there's an exodus from Sugarbush to New York. But since I fly, I don't have to leave until Monday morning. So I have the pleasure of a couple extra ski runs down Organgrinder trail and another dinner at the Sugarbush Inn. Later, downstairs in the Sapbucket, Ruth (Skitch's wife) and I usually run into friends and before we know it, we are at the piano for a group-singing. And on the way home we generally stop for a nightcap at Gallagher's Wheelwright and Cider Mill —a very interesting place made out of a huge old barn. I get this extra time at Sugarbush, plus the added *fun,* only because I'm able to fly my own plane."

Many vacation areas hold special flying events. For example, each year the Bahamas Development Board, Nassau Flying Club and other aviation boosters in the Islands sponsor a week long Bahamas Treasure Hunt. This event is an exercise in ground spotting. Each contestant is given a map, and instructions on the location of clues, along with a questionnaire to fill out. The main clues to be spotted from the air are five-foot Dayglo letters. Extra points are also given for locating and describing certain landmarks and markers along the way. There are additional clues to be spotted on foot at the various overnight stops. These consist of one-foot letters placed in unlikely spots.

111

The actual hunt lasts five days, with leisurely flights from island to island. To eliminate crowding at some of the out island stops, and the possibility of 50 or more planes all buzzing around the same clue simultaneously, the contestants are divided into sections. All contestants agree that the Bahamas Treasure Hunt is *fun*.

Group fly-ins are *fun,* too. One of the best organized social groups of private pilots in the United States is the "Fly for Funsters" of Santa Monica, California. This organization was started by Mr. and Mrs. Robert Gunnell of Gunnell Aviation, Inc., a few years ago and its members fly to some point of interest every 8 to 10 weeks all year round. Mrs. Gunnell—better known as Gil—explains that "Fly for Funsters" is a group, not a club, since they have no officers, don't collect dues, and have no by-laws. They just like to fly and have fun. Some in the group don't even own a plane. They rent them.

Let's fly along with one "Fly for Funster" as he describes his 950-mile weekend trip (one way) from Santa Monica, California to Baja, Mexico, as follows:

"Twenty-eight planes left on Thursday and our first stop was Mexicali, where we landed in order to clear Mexican customs and refuel for the remaining 760-mile flight to the tip of Baja. After an hour's delay to wait for passengers on a Mexican airliner to check through the same customs office, we took off, anxious to join the other members of the flying party at our destination—Hotel Cabo San Lucas. However, darkness overtook us before we reached the resort, so we landed at La Paz International Airport and spent the night in that delightful capital of Baja California Spur. Mexican law forbids anyone to fly at night, except IFR.

"The remaining 95 miles from La Paz to the resort the following morning took less than an hour's flying time. We arrived in time to join the other 86 members of the Funsters for breakfast at the hotel. Bob and Gil, as they always do, preceded the group to the resort and had everything arranged for us.

112

"There was a marlin fishing contest for both fishermen and their ladies; a sea turtle race matching brightly painted sea turtles captured by Mexican fishing guides and marlin contestants during the daily fishing excursion; a burro race in which everyone participates, and other social activities of special interest to fliers and guests alike. The whole theme of the fly-ins is fun. And fun everyone has in a big way."

Expenses for fly-ins are shared by all "Fly for Funsters" group members. Usually couples team up and divide flying costs, which actually amount to less than if they'd driven an automobile the same distance. For instance, sharing expenses for renting a single-engine plane which included fuel and oil, for the flight to Cabo San Lucas averaged about $65 per couple. Most planes carry at least four passengers, including the pilot. The airstrip at the hotel was scraped from cactus covered hillside near the resort. Though the strip is dirt, it is quite smooth and is fairly well equipped.

Some flying groups like that of the Mac Flying Club of Long Island specialize in day-long flights. Once a month they have a so-called "formation" flight which may include breakfast at Mount Pocono (Pennsylvania), lunch in Windsor Locks (Connecticut) and *Coq-au-Vin* at East Hampton (New York). Other day flights include a visit to Corning Glass Center, a bowling tournament in Providence, a fishing contest at Martha's Vineyard, etc.

One of the major events of this club is the annual Mac Air Rally which takes place on July 4th. In this contest, good pilotage, proficiency, and knowledge of aircraft are important—not the throttle against the panel. Six airports in six different states are covered, but at five of them only a touch-and-go procedure is employed. Everyone refuels at the same airport. The planes leave MacArthur Airport at five minute intervals, proceed on the course to the various designated airports in the proper order, and return to starting point some five hours or so later. While the winner is the pilot who covers the course

A flying family trip may be a weekend jaunt within 500 miles of home or it may be an extended vacation covering large sections of the country.

in the shortest amount of time, the important factor is fuel consumption per hour. If you use more than five gallons of gas per flight-hour in a Cessna 150, for instance, you would be disqualified. Five is the magic number for this class of aircraft, but the magic number for fuel consumption for other types varies and usually runs higher. Prizes are given by Mac-aire Aviation Corporation, sponsor of the event, to the winner of each class, plus to the overall champion. You don't have to be Steve Canyon to win, just a good weekend-type pilot, because *fun* is most important in the Mac Air Rally. By the way, the whole family can go on the rally flight.

It's impossible, of course, to describe all the possible trips and uses that an airplane can be put to. We have just made random suggestions in this chapter to start you thinking as to ways to make the most of that license you've earned. Here's a check-list of a dozen tips for putting the business family plane to work on weekends, days off, and vacations:

. . . Visit children away at school

. . . Visit out-of-town friends and family

. . . Go shopping in the big city

. . . Get away from it all at an out-of-the-way recreation spot

. . . Attend school or family reunions out of town

. . . Attend conventions with husband (or wife)

. . . Visit museums, historical landmarks

. . . Attend concerts, art exhibitions, theatres in metropolitan areas

. . . Plan special weekend trips for very important guests

. . . Attend out-of-town sporting events, "major league" baseball, football, basketball, golf, etc.

. . . Go exploring (old trails, etc.)

. . . Go sight-seeing.

And do it all in a business/family airplane!

Chapter 7

But Can I Afford the
Joys of Private Flying?

THERE's no question about it—flying your own plane is fun, safe, healthful, interesting, prestige building, useful, and economical. But, there's still one *big* question: Can *I* afford the joys of private flying?

While it's not so cheap as taking the bus, maybe, flying your own plane doesn't necessarily mean that you have to be rolling in "green stuff." If you don't believe me, just drive up to any airport parking lot where there's general aviation facilities, and what do you see? Cadillacs? Chryslers? MGs? Occasionally. But they're difficult to locate in among the Fords, Dodges and Volkswagens. These people can afford to fly and so can you.

There are several paths which you can follow. For instance, you can purchase your own airplane—either alone or with a few friends by using a joint ownership plan. You can rent one. Or you can join a flying club. Your choice will depend on not one, but several factors: the amount of money you wish (or have) to spend; the number of hours a year you expect to fly; your experience in flying an airplane, and your proximity to an airport with the proper facilities. Let's see if we can help you make the decision.

But, before seeing what path is best for you, first take a look at four broad classifications from which you can

Six-place single-engine aircraft, now gaining rapidly in popularity, offer spacious, economical transportation for groups such as this fishing party.

get at least an idea of what type airplane will best suit your needs. The following breakdown was prepared by the Aerospace Industries Association:

CLASS I.   One- to two-place, having a gross weight of 1,500 pounds or less. Powered with 65 to 150 hp engines, with speeds from 70 to 125 mph. In this group are the aircraft most often used for training, for light agricultural use, and for sport and family flying. Many have a small seat in the back for two children.

CLASS II.   Three- to four-place, weighing from 2,100 to 3,000 pounds and powered with engines from 125 to 230 hp. These are good "cross-country" aircraft, able to maintain cruising speeds from 125 to 180 mph and fly 3 to 4 hours without refueling. Could be considered the typical family airplane.

CLASS III.   Four- to six-place, having a gross weight of from 2,200 to 4,600 pounds and powered with engines from 175 to 309 hp. These aircraft can cruise at speeds from 140 to 225 mph.

CLASS IV.   Four- to ten-place, twin-engine light transports, with 150 to 500 hp engines. These aircraft, in demand by business corporations, have a cross-country speed of from 150 to 280 mph, 4 to 7 hour flight time without refueling.

YOUR OWN AIRPLANE

Buying an airplane of your own is the ideal choice, but it's also the most expensive. When first visiting your local aircraft dealer, you may be shocked. New airplanes are not cheap. Neither is that so-called "family cruising boat" and that can be used only a few months of the year. As a matter of fact, the prices of a typical family cabin cruiser and an airplane are comparable.

Of course, when you first look at an airplane on the dealer's strip, the question that surely comes to mind is why are they so expensive. There's just about as much metal and glass as the average automobile, but it costs twice or more as much. Basically, there are three reasons for this.

119

Favorite hunting and camping grounds are more accessible in a private airplane. Modern aircraft have plenty of room for people, baggage, and equipment. Yes, the dogs can ride along, too.

120

First, there's the volume of production. Whereas the nation's auto manufacturers turn out more than 8,000,-000 units a year, the general aviation industry builds only 16,000. The higher the volume, of course, the lower the unit cost. Also, a great deal of handwork goes into the construction of an airplane, thus further increasing the unit cost.

The second factor is the exacting control of aircraft quality not only of the finished product, but also of a thousand tiny construction steps along the way. This is demanded not only by the FAA, but also by the manufacturers. In fact, most manufacturers build to specifications even more stringent than those required by the FAA. What this means is that numberless time- and money-consuming inspections—both government and manufacturer—must be performed, from the original design up to the last rivet. The reason? Safety.

The third is that the cost of the specialized equipment such as radio gear and the basic flight instruments. While a plane can be bought without this equipment, most pilots prefer it on cross-country hops.

We're not going to quote any prices for the various class of planes since they vary according to manufacturer and the equipment supplied. As in the case of flight schools, we suggest that you visit the *authorized* dealers in your area. The actual purchase of a new airplane is so similar to the mechanics of buying a car that describing the steps involved would be superfluous.

Airplanes, like automobiles, are available used. But, unlike cars, used airplanes have the built-in safeguard of the FAA's yearly (or every one-hundred-hour) inspections. This means that a plane, to maintain an airworthiness certificate, must have passed FAA inspections in the preceding year. While these aren't a guarantee that the plane has no defects at all, they do insure that the basic airframe and power plant are sound and flyable. The odometer on a car can be turned back, but any plane's logbook and certificate have to be accurately maintained (and kept with the plane), and distortions or oversights are subject to heavy penalties. The result of this inspection system has been to make flying safer and more economical for everybody. But, even with the FAA safeguards, it's wise to get a skilled aviation mechanic to inspect it before you close the deal.

Financing an airplane, new or used, on time is handled very much like automobile financing. Usually a ten to twenty-five per cent down payment is required, depending on the cost of the airplane, with up to five years to pay. If you buy a plane, especially a new one before you have your license, the dealer will quite frequently include all lessons straight on through to your solo flight and sometimes private license at no cost. This is the most economical way to learn to fly and is the one some business fliers use when their firms have established the need for a plane.

Speaking of business, the popularity of the joint business/family plane is seen in the growing membership in organizations of pilots within specified professions or businesses. The National Association of Flying Physicians recently held its annual fly-in get-together. The National Association of Flying Osteopathic Physicians sponsors a seminar on aviation medicine each year. The International Flying Farmers Association has chapters throughout the United States and Canada. Flying lawyers (Lawyer-Pilots Association) call themselves the "Legal Eagles." And a small but old and highly respected association is the "Sky Pilots," made up of clergymen who use aircraft to minister to congregations in sparsely settled areas of North America.

The Aircraft Owners & Pilots Association (AOPA) is the world's largest service organization for pilots and owners of general aviation aircraft and is dedicated to the interest and welfare of all who fly. Its membership is made up of more than 100,000 private pilots and/or aircraft owners and is considered as the "voice of general aviation."

Speaking of flying organizations, another one that is worthy of mention is the Civil Air Patrol (CAP). This group is a civilian auxiliary of the United States Air Force and provides aviation education of private citizens with adequate facilities to assist in meeting local and national emergencies. It also encourages and fosters civil aviation in local communities.

OPERATIONAL COSTS

When you own your own airplane there are certain operational costs that occur. These, however, are sometimes difficult to figure and vary throughout the country to a degree. Aside from fuel and oil, the major operating costs are: storage, insurance, and airplane and engine maintenance.

Storage. The cost of hangar space can be as low as $15 a month, as high as $75. An outdoor tie-down is much cheaper, and is the usual thing in southern and southwest states. It's unwise, however, in our northern states in colder months. A tie-down usually runs from $10 to $25 per month.

Away from home, you'll usually pay $1 to $2 a day for a tie-down. At many airports it's even free.

Insurance. Figure about five to seven per cent of the airplane's value for complete insurance coverage. But remember that the variables are infinite and depend not only on the insurance company, but on the type of airplane, its home airport, the kind of weather that predominates in the area, whether or not the airplane is hangared, and the experience level of the pilot.

Aircraft insurance is similar to automobile coverage. The so-called *hull insurance* covers any physical damage to the airplane. It has deductibles—usually two: in motion; not in motion—like an auto body coverage policy, but its rates run higher than auto rates because the possibility of total loss on a plane in an accident is greater than a car. On the other hand, *public-liability insurance* is generally lower than for an automobile. A safe rule is about $50,000 for each passenger seat. Remember that insurance payments are usually combined with ownership payments.

Another consideration is your *personal insurance*. In recent years, most insurance companies have not discriminated against pilots by imposing "exclusions" related to flying. The fact of the matter is that most insurance companies have now decided that there is less risk in private flying than in many other activities which are not excluded. So, if your policies are fairly recent, you probably are covered. But, if you have policies ten or more years old, there may be a clause that excludes private flying from being covered. Often, you can get these clauses written out of the policies merely by requesting it. In some cases, there may be a slight increase in premium.

An increasing number of insurance companies are establishing a compromise between the old and the new. Recognizing that experience is an important factor in flying safely, these companies charge a somewhat higher premium until the pilot has 400 to 600 hours flying time (the figure varies from one company to another) and then reverts to the normal rate. A common alternative, however, is the purchase of special low cost "pilot insurance" which covers private flying and nothing else. (For information on such policies, write to the Aircraft Owners and Pilots Association, Washington, D. C. 20014.)

In any case, you should check with your own insurance agent. He'll be able to tell you how you stand and will work out a suitable program for you.

Airplane and Engine Maintenance. Airplanes, like automobiles, require regular care. This routine maintenance, repairs, and replacements runs $200 or more a year. This includes the regular 25 hour checks, but does not cover the required 100 hour and annual inspection which may range from $100 up. In addition, engines must be completely overhauled at stipulated intervals—usually after each 800 to 1,200 flying hours (depending on specifications) at a cost that can run from around $800 to more than $2,000. But remember that 1,000 hours of air travel in an airplane that cruises at 130 mph is equivalent to
124

130,000 miles of travel. (Most automobiles are ready for the junk heap—not overhaul—after traveling such a distance.) Owners usually make an allowance of about 80¢ to $2 for every hour of flying time to pay for these overhauls.

While the FAA regulations protect you by requiring stipulated periodic inspections, you're on your own between inspections, and here is where prudence is important. The prudent owner accepts the fact that it's going to cost money to keep his airplane in safe and top operating condition, and is never so short-sighted that he tries to cut corners on basic maintenance costs. Remember that the registered owner is responsible for keeping the maintenance records of the aircraft and each engine; for presenting the records for required entries each time of inspection or maintenance; and for making the records available for inspection by the FAA or the Civil Aeronautics Board. If the aircraft is sold, the records must be transferred to the new owner.

But let's do a little quick figuring on the costs of a typical four-place family plane (Class II) like the Cessna Skyhawk. You can manipulate these costs upward or downward by applying your own model airplane, your own personal flying desires, your own budget flexibility, and certain rates at your airport. Here is the budget for a typical Skyhawk based on national cost averages (by the way, the costs have tended to remain fairly stable over the years, or even go down slightly):

COST OF OPERATION FOR CESSNA SKYHAWK

	Per Year	Per Hour	Per Hour	Per Hour
Flight Hours per Year		300	500	700
Flight Miles per Year (130 mph)		39,000	65,000	91,000
Gasoline: 9.5 gal./hr. @ 40¢/gal.		$3.80	$3.80	$3.80
Oil: 1 pt./hr. plus oil change every 25 hrs. (8 qts. per change) @ 50¢/qt.		$ .41	$ .41	$ .41
Airplane & Engine Maintenance		$1.15	$1.15	$1.15
TOTAL OPERATIONAL COSTS (listed above)		$5.36	$5.36	$5.36

Reserve for Engine Overhaul		$1.10	$1.10	$1.10
Storage: @ $40 per month	$480.00			
Insurance—a guide for the following coverage:				
All risks hull coverage (Deductibles: In motion $250—Not in motion $50) (1st yr.—Less in subsequent yrs.)	$487.20			
Liability Coverage (Single limit $250,000 policy)	$124.00			
TOTAL INSURANCE (Industrial private business & pleasure use by a qualified pilot)	$611.20	$ 2.04	$1.22	$ .87
Cost per Hour		$10.10	$8.64	$8.02
Cost per Mile cruise at 75% power, 130 mph		$ .078	$.067	$.062

The above figures point out two important facts. First, about the only way anyone can say that an airplane is not economical—and get away with it—is when they talk about an airplane that isn't used. But the same thing can be said for an automobile. It—or almost anything else—is expensive if it's left idle. Second is that the modern four-place, low-cost private airplane operated between 300 and 500 hours per year provides air transportation comparable in comfort and operating cost to the modern automobile, but takes less than one-third the time.

TIME AND DISTANCE COMPARISON*

	Distance (Miles)		Time in Hours	
FROM: Wichita, Kansas	Most Direct Highways	Direct Air	Auto[1]	Cessna Skyhawk[2]
TO: Kansas City	200	180	4	1:25
Omaha	318	260	7	2:00

Dallas	388	340	8	2:35
Memphis	585	460	12	3:30
New Orleans	898	680	20	5:40 GS
Detroit	990	830	22	6:50 GS
Chicago	733	600	18	5:05 GS
Denver	519	450	12	3:25
Los Angeles	1498	1250	36	11:00 1 L
				2 GS

KEY: GS—Gas Stop . . . 1/2 hour
     L—Lunch Stop . . . 1 hour
     Where Gas and Lunch Stop was combined . . . 1 hr.

* These represent only a few examples in one locality. Compare your locality and where you travel. Many times airlines or train schedules are inconvenient, or perhaps your destination isn't even served.
[1] Auto time: 50 mph average with minimum time allowance for stops.
[2] Cessna Skyhawk: 130 mph average with minimum time allowance for stops.

It is true that airline time between major cities will be less—in some cases substantially less—than in a private plane. However, the personal airplane offers the advantage of being ready to go when you're ready and not dependent on a fixed schedule. Also remember that travel to hundreds of cities off the beaten major airways paths will almost always be less in a private plane.

If you (or your company) have a legitimate business use for a private plane, that portion of flying done in the course of business can be claimed as a business expense, as can portions of ownership and depreciation costs. Full particulars should be checked at the nearest Internal Revenue Service office (look under *U. S. Govt.* in your local telephone directory). For depreciation costs, consult your tax authority. To estimate it per hour or per mile, divide the annual depreciation amount by the annual hours or miles. Since airplanes are carefully maintained and models don't change appreciably each year, most business/family planes tend to hold their value and depreciate a great deal slower than automobiles. Actually, airplanes have a long life expectancy. Many of the aircraft flying today are 15

127

to 35 years old. In other words, if a plane is given good care, it will last almost indefinitely.

Does the cost of owning an airplane seem high? Well just figure out what it would cost you to keep that thirty-foot cabin cruiser you may have your eye on. And remember when that boat is beached high and dry during the long, cold winter months, accumulating storage costs, you can be sailing in the blue with your airplane, traveling to the Caribbean with your family on vacation, or winging your way to a wonderful ski weekend.

AIRPLANE RENTALS

After adding up depreciation and operating costs, many a pilot discovers that it doesn't pay him to own his own plane—especially if he doesn't fly it at least 200 hours a year. Rental rates vary a great deal and depend on the type airplane used: Class I—$12 to $18 an hour; Class II —$16 to $24 an hour; Class III—$22 to $35 an hour; and Class IV—$40 up an hour. Generally, you are charged rent only for the time the plane is actually flown. Rates include gas, oil and insurance. On prolonged trips, where you find refueling operations necessary, you'll be credited for any money spent for fuel upon presentation of the receipts. This also holds true for any maintenance expenses on your rental trips. Tie-down fees at en route or destination airports are generally not included.

Some aircraft service concerns have a so-called "air travelers plan," which offer special low-cost rental rates to those who fly regularly but whose volume of flying doesn't warrant ownership of an aircraft. However, even at standard rates, airplane rental costs compare very favorably with auto fees when figured on a cost per mile basis for the same distance covered. Figuring that a Class I airplane, for example, rents for $15 per hour and cruises at 100 mph, this means that the cost per mile is 15¢. If you *carefully* check the *total* cost per mile of an average auto rental for the same distance, you'll find that is about the same (15¢ a mile) or even more.

While plane rentals automatically eliminate some of the concerns that accompany owning an airplane, there are a few items that must be considered, too. For instance, when you present yourself at a strange airport and display your private license, the operator won't simply toss you the keys to one of his airplanes. He will send you up with one of his checkout pilots to make sure, first of all, that you can fly safely and are familiar with the type of airplane he is renting to you. This involves a flight on dual rates—approximately four to five dollars per hour higher than solo. Usually a ten-minute flight around the field suffices, however, and you're on your own. And once you're on the list as checked out, this formality can be eliminated.

Another consideration is the time minimum imposed on rental aircraft for flights lasting a day or more. When you wish to take an airplane on a cross-country, for example, and stay for a weekend or so, you must pay a minimum fee of about three or four hours' flying time a day, even if you don't actually log that amount.

The most negative consideration, however, is the chance that a plane isn't available when you want it. While plane rentals are commonplace, there are times, especially on weekends, when no planes can be had.

Despite these disadvantages, for the occasional weekend or vacation pleasure pilot, and for some business pilots, rental is often the most economical way to fly. If more than one person is traveling, your costs usually come out equal to or below airline fares, plus you can leave and arrive at hours you choose. In addition, you can make useful detours and "touch downs" at will without added cost. A rental plane can reach thousands of spots not traveled by airlines, plus you usually save time by going direct. In other words, all the benefits of private flying are yours with rentals, except for one. That's one of the big pluses of owning your own plane—it's there waiting *when* you want it.

FLYING CLUBS

The non-profit flying cooperative is one of a growing number of organizations offering members use of an airplane for pleasure or business. A "club" may consist of two persons who pool their resources to buy and maintain a new or used airplane, or it may consist of a number of businessmen or pleasure pilots who jointly own one or more late-model aircraft to be used on business or pleasure trips. The possible combinations are infinite, but the need or the desire to fly is the cement which binds them all. The most obvious advantage of these arrangements is that they permit the cost of airplane ownership to be spread over a broad base and at the same time give partners regular access to convenient air travel.

Possibly one of the best known of the cooperative flying clubs is the Sky Roamers of Burbank, California. It was founded in 1946 by ten persons who pooled money to purchase a trainer-type airplane in which several of them learned to fly. In less than two years, another two aircraft were added. Membership grew steadily, and more and more airplanes were added to the fleet until today the club has over 30. From the beginning, the Sky Roamer has been dedicated to the concept that there exists a vast need for the benefits of cooperative airplane ownership among the many individuals and firms who need the advantages of air transportation but who can't justify sole ownership or who don't wish to incur the cost and limitations of rental.

Within the club are a group of members devoted only to pleasure flying, another group interested only in business flying, and a third (the largest) which flies jointly for business and pleasure. Many members are just learning to fly; others are veteran pilots. Ages range from 16 to a venerable 75. A wide range of businesses and professions is represented within the membership, among them lawyers, doctors, dentists, engineers, real estate brokers, accountants, contractors, and show business personalities.

Women pilots compose abut ten per cent of the club and could probably sustain a flying sorority of their own.

If an "average" Sky Roamer had to be chosen, however, he would be an established businessman in his early forties who is an accomplished, but not a high-time, pilot. More than half of his flying would be for business, but he would also make a number of pleasure trips with his family on weekends and vacations. Because of its location and generally favorable weather, the Los Angeles area is an ideal place from which to stage weekend family trips by air which would be impossible by automobile. Among the more popular destinations are Phoenix and a number of guest ranches in Arizona; Las Vegas; San Francisco; and many places in Baja California and the Mexican mainland. All are within two or three hours by air, but require 8-10 hours driving time.

One-day family outings are becoming more and more popular with members, particularly during the summer. The California beach cities are favorite spots, as are a growing number of family recreation centers which are being built around California airstrips to cater to the flying trade. Golfers in the club frequently make up foursomes and fly to play the many courses in California, Nevada, and Arizona. Vacation trips of several thousand miles by a member and his family aren't uncommon, and at one time or another Sky Roamers aircraft have landed at almost every airport in the United States.

Upon joining the cooperative, each member purchases a negotiable share of stock and thereby earns a voice in the management of the corporation. The stock may be sold at face value should the holder wish to discontinue his membership. Sky Roamers members are placed in one of several classifications according to their flying proficiency, travel needs, and the type of aircraft they wish to fly. The cost of negotiable shares, registration fees, monthly dues, and hourly flying rates vary according to the classification of membership. But, because of its non-profit status, the cooperative is able to offer flying rates far less than those offered commercially. The hourly rate on a Cessna Skyhawk, for example, is $9.00 (including gas and oil). Allowances are built into the rental rates to cover aircraft depreciation and maintenance.

Members operate under very few restrictions, and even these are reasonable ones based on getting the most economical use from the fleet of airplanes. For example, each member is required to use at least 40 flying hours per year and during cross-country flights must log an average of at least two flying hours per day. Safety and training are highly stressed at Sky Roamers. Members are thoroughly trained in the basic skills of flying and safe flying practices, and are encouraged to develop skills and acquire ratings comparable to or approaching that of the professional pilots.

At the other extreme on the cooperative ladder from the Sky Roamers is the informal group of two or more families who own a single plane, sharing the costs as well as the flying time. Such a group, even though small, generally prefers to incorporate in order to limit the liability of individual members. (Plane partnerships are not usually advisable because of the liability consideration.) For example, let's take a look at a foursome club—four owners flying a Cessna Skyhawk approximately 100 hours per year each (13,100 miles) or approximately 400 total aircraft hours per year (52,400 miles). The cost of operation is as follows:

Items	Foursome (400 Hours)	Each Individual (100 Hours)
Fuel and Maintenance:		
Gasoline—9.5 Gals./hr. @ 40¢/Gal.	$1,520.00	$ 380.00
Oil—1 pt./hr. plus oil change every 25 hours (8 qts. per change) at 50¢ per quart	164.00	41.00
Airplane and Engine Maintenance at $1.15 per hours	460.00	115.00

Reserve for Engine Overhaul @ $1.10/hr.	440.00	110.00
TOTAL DIRECT OPERATIONAL COST	$2,584.00	$ 646.00

Fixed Charges per Flight Year

Storage—$40.00 per month	$ 480.00	$ 120.00
Depreciation (Based on purchase price of $14,146.54, straight-line depreciation with $9\frac{1}{2}$ year life and 10% residual value.*	1,340.20	335.05
TOTAL ANNUAL STORAGE COST AND AIRPLANE DEPRECIATION	$1,820.20	$ 455.05

Total Annual Insurance

All Risks (ground and flight), Public Liability	$1,120.00	$ 280.00

Total Cost	$5,524.20	$1,381.05
Miles (Average Cruise Speed— 130 mph)	52,400	13,100
Cost per airplane mile	$ .105	$ .105
Cost per Seat Mile (4 seats)	$ .0263	$ .0263

* Special Tax Consideration may be involved, and your tax counsel should be consulted for treatment for tax purposes.

Your individual initial investment in a foursome club would cost for a 1/4th share in the fully equipped Skyhawk $3,536.64 (full price $14,146.54). If you wished, your share of the airplane could be financed as follows:

Computation of Monthly Finance Payment

Item	One of Foursome
Skyhawk Equipped	$3,536.64
25% Cash Payment	$ 884.16
Balance to Carry	$2,652.48
Interest 6% Annually for 48 months	$ 636.60
Total to Carry	$3,289.08
Amount per Month	$ 68.52

In between organizations like the Sky Roamers and the foursome type flying group are the so-called *typical* flying club. Such a club usually has three to six airplanes—and thirty to forty pilots. Joining will cost anywhere from $250 to $500, which entitles you to one membership share. Then you can reserve any of the planes after checking out in them (many clubs use phone-answering services to keep track of the bookings), and use them either weekdays or weekends. Most clubs limit weekend-long use of any of the planes to once a month. The hourly charge for the planes averages from $9 to $14. Clubs of this type are so popular that you may discover that your local one has a waiting list.

The flying club is often the best compromise between owning and renting an airplane; and it's generally cheaper than either of the others. But, in such an organization you must share the plane with others. You can't simply fly any time you feel like it. Actually both plane rentals and flying clubs are excellent "fill-ins" until the time comes when you feel that you can afford to own an airplane all by yourself.

Chapter 8

The Three R's
and Flying, Too

Peggie Sue's father says she can ride better than any "cowhand" on their large Wyoming ranch. Peggie wants to be a veterinarian. Betty Jean attends an exclusive private school in New England and is deeply interested in music, drama and art. Her ambition is to be an interior decorator. Buck Mahoney goes to high school in Dallas where he has letters in football, basketball and track. Buck likes the outdoors and plans to study engineering.

Although these three teen-agers live in widely separated regions of our land and have diverse interests, they have much in common. They share the same birthday and the common interest does not stop there. Each celebrated his or her sixteenth birthday by flying an airplane alone and satisfying the "solo" requirement.

Admittedly, these young men and women have joined a rather select fraternity of teen-age pilots, but their experiences as pilots are not actually unique. Over 20,000 teen-agers possess the coveted pilot's license, ranging all the way from a student pilot permit up to commercial and even the air transport rating. Teen-agers represent the fastest growing group of pilots in the United States and the number is increasing 48 per cent per year.

What motivates these thousands of young people to achieve competency in the exciting field of flight? Some teen-agers see their career futures in aviation and aerospace. Professional pilots, of course, are needed by the airlines. Corporations which operate their own fleets of aircraft are also seeking qualified personnel. Air taxis, charter operators, flight schools, agricultural applicators, aerial mapping and patrol services, all express concern over the need for young men and women with aviation training.

Industry and government are faced with a need for flight instructors to handle the 193,000 new students who are expected to initiate flight training each year by the end of 1968.

A critical shortage is forecast for licensed airframe and power-plant technicians to maintain a fleet which is expected to reach a figure of between 160,000 and 200,000 active aircraft by 1975. As more and better avionic equipment continues to characterize both commercial and private aviation, the need for electronics specialists is almost without limitation.

Most pilots throughout the country do not fly for pay, since 97 per cent of the single-engine owners fly their own planes. One owner out of four is a professional man or self-employed in technical work. Other heavy owner-pilot groups include: agriculture, sales, manufacturing, construction, real estate, finance, insurance, petroleum and mining. These business and professional men and women use their private aircraft to cover more territory, see more prospects, give better service and make more sales and profits. Pilot skills and knowledge enhance a person's ability to reap the fullest returns from his chosen career or profession.

Others fly for fun. There are few experiences as peaceful and satisfying as breaking the bonds of earth and shattering the quiet of morning as you move down the runway, then feel yourself climb into the air and soar above the tensions of everyday life. Actually, so commonplace and indispensable is flying today that an increasing number of public and private schools at all levels are accepting aviation as part of the curriculum. Some 125 colleges have competitive flying teams which take part in two major national competitions each year under the auspices of the National Intercollegiate Flying Association. Events include precision landing contests, stressing both power-on and power-off techniques. Bomb drops, fuel management races and navigation competition round out the events.

Many universities, like Oklahoma, Middle Tennessee, Ohio State, Illinois, and Southern Illinois, have their own airports and fleets of modern, well-equipped airplanes. Purdue offers a bachelor's degree in aviation, as does Parks College of the University of St. Louis. San Jose State confers a master's degree. Many institutions provide work leading to various engineering degrees in aeronautics, while Oklahoma State University accredits aviation through the College of Education.

Aviation workshops for classroom teachers are conducted at more than 175 colleges each summer. The fast growing complex of junior colleges has turned to aviation as an area suitable for technical training for those who pursue terminal curricula.

The big boom seems to be in our high schools. A study of 120 high schools which offer aviation for credit gives us some clue as to the ingredients that add up to the more successful programs. Some high schools, such as Crescent City, California, have offered aviation, including flight training, since the close of World War II. At the other extreme, some schools offer only a short orientation course.

One major aircraft manufacturer which has conducted an active air-age education program for the past ten years

Horseman Steve Clark, Cannonville, Utah, visits the Cessna Super Skylane at Bryce Canyon. Note the rugged, log hangar and the wind sock sticking straight out.

has developed a complete teaching guide for all levels from kindergarten through college. Information is available from the Air Age Education Department, The Cessna Aircraft Company, Wichita, Kansas. Its recommended program which is becoming generally accepted as meeting accreditation standards and best-fitting into the overall high school activities is one offered for credit and covers 90 class hours of instruction.

Thirty hours are devoted to the place of air transportation in modern living, including counseling and guidance relative to career opportunities. The other 60 hours are divided among the elements which comprise the subjects of ground school and can equip the student to take the FAA written examination for the private pilots rating. It covers:

Principles of Flight	5 hours
Aircraft and Engine Operation	4 hours
Aircraft Performance	4 hours
Navigation and Chart Reading	10 hours
Flight Computer	4 hours
Radio Guidance in VFR Flying	3 hours
Radio Communications	1 hour
Flight Information Publications—Airports	2 hours
Weather	10 hours
Federal Aviation Regulations	10 hours
Structure of Airway System	1 hour
Flight Instruments	3 hours
Attitude Instrument Flying	2 hours
Flight Planning	1 hour

In addition to the above, some of the more successful programs offer at least a flight experience. A normal approach provides this as an option for which the student pays a laboratory fee of perhaps $10.00. Three students, with an instructor in a four-place, single-engine plane, make a flight of 1½ hours, consisting of three 30-minute legs. Each student flies one leg, but is equipped to navigate over the entire course.

Historically, 54 per cent of the high school students who take such a course have continued after completion by enrolling for a solo course through the facilities of a fixed base operator and more than 60 per cent of those who solo do, in fact, complete the private rating within one year. In one rural high school in Oklahoma, every boy in the senior class soloed during the school term.

The interest kindled during high school often sustains itself throughout college years and leads to a full and rewarding career. Martha Smith of Ohio worked in a dealer's office after school and on week-ends to earn flight time. As a college freshman, she continued her training and today is a full-time flight instructor at a major university. Beryl Jones started his training in high school, continued in college and today is a franchised dealer for a major aircraft manufacturer.

Both state and regional accrediting agencies are regularly accepting the validity of aviation-oriented curriculum in our high schools. The North Central Accreditation Association has, over a period of several years, looked favorably upon aviation as a fulfilment of science requirements or as an elective acceptable for college entrance.

Bobby Netzley of Dayton had logged over 200 flying hours in the United States, Canada and Mexico long before she learned to drive. She often said, "My biggest problem was getting to the airport." Bobby and thousands of other young people who started to fly during their teens typify the foresighted youth who recognize that ability to compete is improved by willingness to prepare, and then to contribute in a world that is increasingly geared to air transportation. The youth who closes his eyes to the existence of a new age will arrive at the party after everybody else has gone home. Those who try to solve tomorrow's problems with yesterday's tools, training, equipment or concepts cannot hope to be competitive next week, next month or ten years down the road.

Perhaps Kipling contemplated our world when he looked upon the first airplane he had ever seen. It was a crude and primitive affair, but he said, "There is what we call a flying machine. In it, I see what I believe to be the opening verse of the opening page of a chapter that has no end because the subject is without limitation."

Chapter 9

Sky Talk

Glossary of Aviation Terms

AILERONS.   The movable parts of the outer wing surface which change the shape of the wing. This is what causes the airplane to "bank" or turn.

AIRFOILS.   The cross-sectional shape of the propeller, wings, and tail.

AIRFRAME.   The structure of an airplane apart from power plant and accessories.

AIR MARKER.   A sign or mark on the ground so made as to be visible to aircraft, indicating direction to an airport or giving other useful data.

AIRPORT SURVEILLANCE RADAR (ASR).   Radar system used in air traffic control.

AIRSPEED.   The speed of an airplane in relation to the air through which it is passing.

AIR TRAFFIC CONTROL (ATC).   The control of air traffic to maintain its safe, orderly and expeditious movement; its operation is handled by the air traffic controller.

AIRWAY.   A designated air route, regularly traveled by aircraft, and provided with air-navigation aids and governed by flight rules, between points on the earth's surface.

AIRWORTHY.   The status of being in condition suitable for safe flight.

ALTIMETER.   An instrument for indicating the altitude of an airplane above sea level by measuring atmospheric pressure.

ALTITUDE.   The elevation of an airplane. This may be specified as above sea level, or above the ground over which it flies.

ANEMOMETER.   A device for measuring the velocity of the wind, in common use at airports.

ANNUAL INSPECTION. The airframe and engine inspection of an airplane by a certificated mechanic, required annually by regulations.

APPROACH. An act or instance of bringing an airplane in to a land; also an access way through which an airplane is brought into land.

APPROACH PATTERN. The flight pattern flown by an airplane in making an approach to a landing. Also called a *landing pattern*.

APRON. An area, generally paved, for parking or handling airplanes.

ARTIFICIAL HORIZON. A flight instrument that shows the pitching and banking attitudes of an airplane with respect to the horizon.

ATTITUDE. The position of an airplane considering the inclination of its axes in relation to the horizon.

AUTOMATIC PILOT. An electronic device which operates the airplane automatically. Same as *autopilot*.

AXIS. The theoretical line extending through the center of gravity of an airplane in each major plane: fore and aft, crosswise, and up and down. These are the longitudinal, lateral, and vertical axes.

BANK. To tip, or roll about the longitudinal axis of the airplane. Banks are incident to all properly executed turns.

BEARING. The horizontal direction of an object.

BIRD. Common expression for an aircraft.

BLIND. Flying under conditions of low visibility; generally using instruments and radio aids.

CEILING. The height of the base of the clouds above the ground. Also the maximum altitude the airplane is capable of obtaining under standard conditions.

CENTER OF GRAVITY. The point within an airplane through which, for balance purposes, the total force of gravity is considered to act.

CHECKLIST. A list of items requiring attention for various flight operations.

144

CHECK POINT. In air navigation, a prominent landmark on the ground, either visual or radio, which is used to establish the position of an airplane in flight.

CIRCUIT BREAKER. A device which takes the place of a fuse in breaking an electrical circuit in case of an overload. Most aircraft circuit breakers can be reset by pushing a button, in case the overload was temporary.

CLEARANCE. An authorization, verbal or otherwise, to depart from an airport or airfield or to fly a given path under specified conditions.

CLIMB-OUT. The climb made directly after take-off.

CLOUD BASE. The lower surface of a cloud.

CLOUD DECK. The upper surface of a cloud.

COMPASS BEARING. Bearing measured relative to magnetic north.

COMPASS HEADING. A heading measured relative to magnetic north.

COMPASS, MAGNETIC. A device for determining the direction of the earth's magnetic field. Subject to local disturbances, the compass will indicate the direction to the north magnetic pole.

COMPASS ROSE. The circular card on a mariner's compass on which are marked the 32 points of direction and the 360 degrees of the circle.

CONTROLS. The devices used by a pilot in operating an airplane.

CONTROL SURFACES. Hinged airfoils exposed to the air flow which control the attitude of the airplane and which are actuated by use of the controls in the airplane.

CONTROL TOWER. An elevated structure at an airport from which air traffic entering and leaving the field is controlled.

COURSE. A predetermined or intended route or direction to be followed during a flight.

COWL. The top portion of the front part of the body of a plane to which are attached the windshield and instrument board.

CROSS-COUNTRY. A flight out of the immediate area . . . just like taking a trip across the country in a car.

CROSSWIND. A wind blowing across the line of flight of an airplane.

CRUISE CONTROL. The procedure for the operation of an airplane, and its power plants, to obtain the maximum efficiency on extended flights.

CRUISING AIRSPEED. The true airspeed at which an airplane cruises.

DEAD RECKONING. The estimating or determining of position by advancing an earlier known position by the application of direction, speed data, and time.

DEVIATION. The error induced in a magnetic compass by steel structure, electrical equipment and similar disturbing factors in the airplane.

DRAG. Force opposing the motion of the airplane through the air.

DRIFT. Deflection of an airplane from its intended course by action of the wind.

ELEVATION. Height or altitude above sea level.

ELEVATOR. A hinged, horizontal control surface used to raise or lower the tail in flight.

EMPENNAGE. Term used to designate the entire tail group of an airplane, including the fixed and movable tail surfaces.

ESTIMATED TIME OF ARRIVAL (ETA). The predicted time at which an airplane in flight will reach a given point, usually its destination.

FIN. A fixed airfoil to increase the stability of an airplane. Usually applied to the vertical surface to which the rudder is hinged.

FIXED LANDING GEAR. A landing gear that remains fixed in the same position at all times.

FLAPS. The hinged surfaces located near the wing trailing edge which increase the camber and lift of the wing. They slow the forward motion of the airplane by increasing drag or air friction.

FLARE OUT. The airplane is "flared out" at the moment

just before touch down. It is simply the act of leveling out the flight path of the airplane parallel to the runway.

FLIGHT PLAN. A detailed outline of a proposed flight usually filed with FAA Flight Service Station before a cross-country flight.

FLOAT. A buoyant water-tight structure which is a part of the "landing gear" of a seaplane.

FORCED LANDING. A landing necessitated by some adverse circumstance.

FREQUENCY. This applies to the radio on your airplane. It is a term that simply means the dial setting that you select for radio information and instructions.

FULL RICH. A fuel-air mixture setting providing the maximum amount of fuel flow.

FUSELAGE. The body to which the wings, landing gear, and tail are attached.

GLIDE. Sustained forward flight in which speed is maintained only by the loss of altitude.

GLIDE RATIO. The ratio of the horizontal distance traveled to the vertical distance descended in a glide (as 10 miles to 1 mile).

GROUND RUN. The take-off and landing runs of an airplane on the ground.

GROUND SCHOOL. A school that gives nonflying instruction in various subjects related to flying.

GROUND SPEED. The speed of an airplane relative to the ground, or locations on the ground.

HEADING. The horizontal direction in which your airplane points as it flies through the air.

HEAD WIND. A wind blowing from directly ahead, on the nose of the airplane.

HOLD. To circle or fly about in a particular pattern near a specified point while waiting for permission or instructions to land or to proceed along a course.

HOOD. A device used in instrument flying practice which prevents you from seeing outside the plane.

ICING. The action or process by which atmospheric moisture is deposited as ice on the airplane.

INSTRUMENT FLIGHT. It means that the pilot will rely entirely on his instruments and radio to tell him the attitude and location of the airplane, its speed, etc. During this type of flight a pilot does not refer to visual reference points . . . just the instrument panel.

INSTRUMENT LANDING SYSTEM (ILS). A radio-guidance and communication system that guides airplanes through approaches, letdowns, and landing under conditions of poor or no visibility.

INSTRUMENT RATING. A rating authorizing you to perform instrument flight.

KNOT. A unit of speed equalling one nautical mile per hour.

LANDING. The act of terminating flight and bringing the airplane to rest.

LANDING AREA. Any area suitable for the landing of an airplane.

LANDING GEAR. The wheels and axles, and struts of an airplane.

LANDING LIGHT. A light, or lights, mounted into the airplane's wings or nose and employed to light up the runway surface during a night landing.

LAND PLANE. An airplane designed to rise from and alight on the ground.

LEADING EDGE. The forward edge of any airfoil.

LEAN. As in a lean or thin fuel to air mixture.

LEG. One of the straight-line portions of a traffic pattern. Also a distinct segment, as between landings, of a cross-country flight.

LETDOWN. The act of letting down, especially the gliding descent of an airplane from cruising altitude prior to an approach or landing.

LIFT. The supporting force induced by the dynamic reaction of air against the wing. The upward force, which acts on an airplane when it is in flight.

LIGHT GUN. An intense, narrowly-focused spotlight with which a green, red, or white signal may be directed at any selected airplane in the traffic pattern on or about an airport. Usually used in control towers.

LOG. To make a flight-by-flight record of all operations of an airplane, engine, or pilot, listing flight time, area of operation, and other pertinent information. These records are kept in a *logbook*.

MAGNETIC NORTH. The direction north as indicated by a magnetic compass.

MAGNETO. The device which supplies electrical current for the self-contained ignition system of an airplane. Same as *mag*.

MANEUVER. Any planned motion of an airplane in the air or on the ground.

NOSE WHEEL. A swivelling or steerable wheel mounted forward in tricycle-landing-geared airplanes.

ORIENTATION. The act of fixing position or attitude by visual or other reference.

OVERCONTROL. To move your airplane's controls more than is necessary for desired performance.

OVERSHOOT. To fly beyond a designated area or mark.

PANEL. Like the dashboard on your car . . . it contains the instruments that allow you to read height, attitude, speed, etc., of the airplane.

PATTERN. This is the system of approaches and exits "patterned" to regulate incoming and out-going air traffic. It is much like the instructions that you find on a highway indicating one-way streets, left turns, etc.

PILOT. One who operates the controls of an airplane in flight.

PILOTAGE. Air navigation by visual reference to landmarks.

PITOT TUBE. A tube exposed to the air stream for measuring impact pressure. It registers indicated airspeed.

POSITION. The location of an airplane with respect to geographical coordinates, such as town or city, or a topographical feature or landmark.

POSITION REPORT. A report given by a pilot in flight to a Flight Service Station giving its position and other data such as speed, heading, etc.

POWER APPROACH. A landing approach in which the plane is under power.

POWER LANDING. A landing during which the airplane is under power until it touches down.

PRECISION APPROACH RADAR (PAR). Radar system used in an airport traffic control system that permits guiding an airplane onto the runway.

PRE-FLIGHT. The inspection of an airplane immediately prior to take-off . . . similar to the inspection that you might make on a car before a trip, with the exception that the aircraft pre-flight is more thorough.

PUSHER. An airplane in which the propeller is mounted aft of the engine, and pushes the air away from it.

PYLON. A prominent mark, or point, on the ground used as a fix in precision maneuvers.

RADAR. The detection of objects (usually aircraft) and measurement of their bearing and distance by their reflection of radio signals.

RECOVERY. The action of an aircraft returning, or being restored to its initial position after a maneuver.

RESTRICTED AREA. An area in which hazards to flight exist, to be flown over only by permission of the proper authority.

ROLL-OUT. The act of leveling the wings after a banked turn.

RUDDER. A hinged, vertical, control surface used to induce or overcome yawing moments about the vertical axis.

RUDDER PEDALS. Controls within the airplane by means of which the rudder is actuated.

RUN-UP. What you do before you take the airplane off the ground. It is like warming up your car. In the case of an airplane, it is done to check to see that the engine is functioning properly.

RUNWAY.   A strip, either paved or improved, on which take-offs and landings are effected.

SEAPLANE.   An airplane equipped to rise from and alight on the water. Usually used to denote an airplane with detachable floats, as contrasted with a flying boat.

SECTIONAL.   A detailed part of an aeronautic chart showing a great many landmarks and reference points . . . much like a road map which gives detailed sections of large cities.

SEQUENCE REPORT.   The weather report transmitted hourly to all teletype stations, and available at all FAA Flight Service Stations and weather bureaus.

SHIP.   Common expression for any aircraft.

SIDESLIP.   A sideways movement of an airplane in the direction of a lowered wing when opposite rudder is applied.

SKID.   The turning motion of an airplane inside an intended path caused by excessive application of rudder toward the direction of the turn.

SLIP.   The turning motion of an airplane outside an intended path caused by insufficient application of rudder toward the direction of the turn.

SLIPSTREAM.   The current of air driven backwards by the propeller.

SOLO.   Piloting the airplane while you are the lone occupant. Also used to indicate the first such flight.

SPIN.   A prolonged stall in which an airplane rotates about its center of gravity while it descends, usually with its nose well down.

SPIRAL.   A prolonged gliding or climbing turn during which more than a 360° change of direction is effected.

STABILITY.   The tendency of an airplane in flight to remain in straight, level, upright flight, or to return to this attitude, if displaced, without attention of the pilot.

STABILIZER.   The fixed airfoil of an airplane used to increase stability; usually, the aft fixed horizontal surface to which the elevators are hinged.

151

STALL. The condition under which air flowing over a wing does not create sufficient lift to maintain altitude.

SWINGING THE COMPASS. Checking and compensating for the indications of an installed compass by comparing them with an accurate compass rose laid out on the ground.

TAIL GROUP. The airfoil members of the assembly located at the rear of an airplane.

TAIL SECTION. The rear section or portion of a fuselage, usually understood to include the tail group.

TAIL WIND. A wind blowing from directly behind the airplane.

TAKE-OFF DISTANCE. The distance required for the take-off run of an airplane under given conditions.

TAKE-OFF RUN. The movement between the point of accelerating for the take-off and the point at which the airplane becomes airborne.

TAKE-OFF SPEED. The airspeed at which an airplane normally becomes airborne under given conditions.

TAXI. To operate an airplane under its own power on the ground.

TAXIWAY. The "road" prepared for taxiing.

THROTTLE. The hand throttle on an airplane is like the gas pedal or accelerator on your car. It is the control that makes the engine run faster or slower.

THRUST. The forward force provided by the engine acting through a propeller in conventional airplanes.

TOUCH-AND-GO LANDING. A landing in which the aircraft touches down, and takes off right away without coming to a complete stop.

TOUCH DOWN. To make contact between the landing gear and the runway.

TRAFFIC PATTERN. A prescribed pattern to be followed by an airplane in the air about an airport.

TRICYCLE LANDING GEAR. A landing gear arrangement which consists of two main wheels and a nose wheel.

TRIM TAB. A movable part of a control surface which

allows the pilot to set, or "trim," the attitude of the airplane and maintain it.

TRUE BEARING.   Bearing measured relative to true north.

TRUE HEADING.   Heading measured relative to true north.

TRUE NORTH.   The direction of the geographic North Pole.

TURN.   An act of changing horizontal direction.

UNDERSHOOT.   To fall short of designated area or mark.

VARIATION.   The difference in direction between the geographic North Pole and the magnetic north pole.

VENTURI.   A tube with a restricted throat, mounted within the propeller's slip stream to provide suction to operate flight instruments. Same as *Venturi Tube*.

VISIBILITY.   The greatest horizontal distance which prominent objects on the ground can be seen. (Used to denote weather conditions.)

VISUAL FLIGHT.   Indicates that the pilot is using visual reference points in order to determine the position of the airplane.

WEATHER-VANE.   The tendency of an airplane on the ground to face into the wind, due to its effect on the vertical surfaces of the tail group.

WIND SHIFT.   An abrupt change in the direction of the wind.

WIND SOCK.   A cloth sleeve, mounted aloft at an airport to use for estimating wind direction and velocity.

WIND TEE.   An indicator for wind or traffic direction at an airport.

WING.   The largest surface on the airplane whose main function is to provide lift for the airplane to fly.

WING TIP.   The end of the wing farthest from the fuselage, or cabin.

ZOOM.   To zoom is to climb for a short time at an angle greater than the normal climbing angle, the airplane being carried upward by momentum.

153

Index

Color pictures following page 32